TRANSPORT AND ROAD RESEARCH LABORATORY
Department of Transport

STATE-OF-THE-ART REVIEW 1

AIR POLLUTION FROM ROAD VEHICLES

by L H Watkins

LONDON: HMSO

ISBN 0 11 551000 1

The views expressed in this review are not necessarily
those of the Department of Transport

HMSO publications are available from:

HMSO Publications Centre
(Mail and telephone orders only)
PO Box 276, London, SW8 5DT
Telephone orders 071-873 9090
General enquiries 071-873 0011
(queuing system in operation for both numbers)

HMSO Bookshops
49 High Holborn, London, WC1V 6HB   071-873 0011 (counter service only)
258 Broad Street, Birmingham, B1 2HE   021-643 3740
Southey House, 33 Wine Street, Bristol, BS1 2BQ   (0272) 264306
9-21 Princess Street, Manchester, M60 8AS   061-834 7201
80 Chichester Street, Belfast, BT1 4JY   (0232) 238451
71 Lothian Road, Edinburgh, EH3 9AZ   031-228 4181

HMSO's Accredited Agents
(see Yellow Pages)

and through good booksellers

Contents

Preface

The air pollution caused by vehicle exhaust emissions first caused concern in California in the 1960s. California has one of the highest rates of car ownership in the world, and this coupled with their geographical and climatic conditions, produced the notorious photochemical smogs generated by atmospheric reactions between the exhaust pollutants. To combat the problem, they introduced the first emission control standards for road vehicles and they are still in the forefront of communities pressing for ever more stringent emission limits. At the same time in the UK, air quality was dramatically improving. Clean Air Acts published in the 1950s had successfully reduced emissions from domestic coal burning and industrial emissions were coming under tighter control. But, as elsewhere, road traffic was growing rapidly and the problems it caused were receiving increasing attention. Regulations limiting vehicle emission rates in the EEC were first introduced in 1970 and have since been amended several times to bring in improved test procedures and lower limits. The standards currently under consideration by the Commission of the European Communities will effectively bring the EEC into line with the USA (though it must be said that the American situation is not static and that their standards will no doubt be reduced in the future).

As scientific research has progressed, perceptions about the relative importance of the various effects of traffic generated pollution have changed. Initial concerns were over direct health effects on humans. Carbon monoxide and lead were known toxins abundantly produced in vehicle exhausts. Other potentially harmful compounds were found in exhaust gases, and as epidemiological and clinical research developed it suggested there might be harmful effects at lower and lower concentrations. A variety of organic compounds, in particular, were shown to be mutagenic or carcinogenic. The measures so far taken to reduce emissions have, however, been largely effective in maintaining or improving air quality in spite of the growth in traffic, so these health risks have not worsened. At current levels the UK Department of Health regards them as 'minor and difficult to detect'. But the pollution from traffic has other effects. Oxides of nitrogen add to the acid species in the air, contributing to 'acid rain' and the damage it causes to lakes, vegetation and buildings; in combination with hydrocarbons, they produce ozone and other oxidants that also damage plants; carbon dioxide, carbon monoxide, oxides of nitrogen and hydrocarbons are all directly or indirectly involved in the enhanced 'greenhouse' effect which is causing concern about global warming. Traffic pollution is not the only, or even the most important, contributor to these problems but it is significant and the fastest growing.

The Transport and Road Research Laboratory has studied vehicle derived air pollution since 1970 and has contributed to the research of many of these aspects. Their work, and that of many others is the subject of this review.

1 Introduction

It was only about a century ago that the first workable four-stroke internal combustion engine was invented in Germany by Nikolas Otto, and shortly afterwards Karl Benz and Gottlieb Daimler produced the world's first cars with internal combustion engines. By the beginning of the 20th century various practical car designs were appearing internationally and a great revolution in transport was under way, the number of vehicles on the road increasing rapidly. In the 1920's successful road vehicles operated by compression-ignition (diesel) engines appeared, in due course to become the predominant power source for heavy goods vehicles.

By early in the second world war the world motor vehicle fleet totalled less than 50 million units (Massachusetts Institute of Technology,1984). By 1987 this had grown to 516 million, of which 394 million were passenger cars, and is still rising. World production is running at over 35 million vehicles a year, including 30 million passenger cars.

Many studies (Massachusetts Institute of Technology, 1984; Tanner, 1983; Wheaton, 1982; OECD, 1982) have been made of this rapid increase to attempt to determine whether there will be a saturation limit, and if so, what will determine it. If every individual theoretically eligible to drive had his or her own car the world fleet would be some 600-630 cars per thousand population. If some individuals kept two, the total might reach 700 per thousand. It is interesting that in the USA by 1980 the actual fleet had already reached 537 per thousand. Taking everything into account it seems likely that the world car population of 394 million in 1987 will probably reach about 536 million in the year 2,000 and will still rise owing primarily to the potential growth in countries like China. The corresponding growth in commercial vehicle numbers is also very difficult to estimate, but if one assumes a growth of only 50 per cent in the same period of time this gives a year 2,000 total of 183 million, and a total world vehicle fleet of 720 million units.

Coming closer to home, comparable figures for the European vehicle population are available (United Nations, 1986). In the United Kingdom the population of passenger cars (by far the most numerous of all types of vehicle) increased from 14.5 million to 18.4 million between 1976 and 1986 (or from 259 per thousand population to 323), and lorries increased during the same period from 1.80 million to 1.94 million. All other countries of Europe, both East and West, showed broadly similar increases.

All these vehicles operate by burning fossil fuel. World consumption of oil fuel by road vehicles increased from about 1.3 billion barrels per year in 1950 to nearly 5.5 billion barrels per year in 1981, and it is still rising. Emission controls in some countries have undoubtedly helped to contain the parallel growth in emissions, but globally vehicle emissions of total pollutants have increased with growing energy consumption, and this problem of air pollution by exhaust emissions has given rise to much worldwide

1

concern and activity, both in the fields of research and development, and also in legislation. In the United Kingdom, as in most other industrialised countries, combustion of fossil fuels for many purposes including transport is the major source of emissions which pollute the air. Table 1.1 published in 1988 by the UK Department of the Environment (1988) sets fuels used by vehicles between 1977 and 1987 into a general context of all other major fuels that are sources of air pollution.

Use of coal fluctuated for many reasons, such as strikes in the coalfields, but by and large remained fairly constant; use of fuel oil fell; use of solid smokeless fuel fell; use of kerosene and gas oil fell; and the only fuel types to show steady increases were some forms of gas, and motor spirit and diesel fuel. Thus although road transport currently accounts for only about 10 per cent of total fossil fuel use, it is one of the sectors showing most rapid growth, and it is particularly important to pay proper attention to the pollution problems of vehicle exhaust gases. These emissions include some that are known to be toxic when absorbed into the body at high concentrations, and although opinions differ as to the seriousness of the risks involved it is clear that the public has become concerned over possible damage to health and that people's subjective reactions are influenced by this concern. In addition to these possible direct effects on health, we have all been becoming aware in recent years of global problems such as acid rain, the so-called ''greenhouse effect'', and others in which vehicle exhaust emissions play a part.

The Transport and Road Research Laboratory set up a small team in 1970 to research into some aspects of vehicle exhaust emissions, and this work still continues. Over the past twenty years the work of the team has made substantial contributions to a rapidly-growing body of knowledge about the effects of, and control of, emissions. Much has been published in reports and papers on individual research projects. From time to time, more comprehensive reviews have appeared, as for example in a previous book on the Environmental Impact of Roads and Traffic by the author of this present review (Watkins, 1981). But in 1990 it is appropriate to bring the strands together into a review of the whole subject of air pollution from road traffic, placing TRRL's work in the wider context of international research on the topic. Nineteen eighty nine marked something of a turning point in emissions control in Europe, since regulations were agreed setting maximum pollutant emissions at levels which can currently only be met by fitting 3-way catalysts to all petrol-engined cars. The subject of air pollution tends to raise strong emotions and to polarise attitudes. The aim of this review is to avoid these pitfalls by presenting the facts, and discussing the findings of the research, in an objective manner.

1.1 Chapter 1 References

DEPARTMENT OF THE ENVIRONMENT, (1988) Digest of environmental protection and water statistics, HMSO, London.

MASSACHUSETTS INSTITUTE OF TECHNOLOGY, (1984) MIT International Program, Report, George Allen and Unwin Ltd, London.

TABLE 1.1

Fossil fuel consumption by type of fuel and consumer[1]
United Kingdom

	1977	1978	1979	1980	1981	1982	1983	1984	1985	1986	1987
Solid Fuels					*Million tonnes*						
Coal:											
Domestic	9.7	8.7	8.9	7.3	6.9	6.7	6.2	4.8	6.5	7.0	5.7
Industry, etc[2]	12.0	11.4	11.8	10.1	9.3	9.4	9.4	8.0	9.5	10.0	9.6
Power stations	80.0	80.6	88.8	89.6	87.2	80.2	81.6	53.4	73.9	82.6	86.2
Gas works[3]	3.2	3.1	2.9	3.0	2.5	2.3	2.1	1.3	2.2	2.0	2.1
Solid smokeless fuel:											
Domestic	4.7	4.5	4.5	4.4	4.0	4.1	3.9	3.2	4.2	3.5	3.5
Industry, etc[4]	3.1	3.1	3.1	2.0	2.0	1.9	1.9	1.8	2.1	2.0	2.0
Liquid Fuels					*Million tonnes*						
Petroleum:											
Motor spirit	17.3	18.3	18.7	19.1	18.7	19.2	19.6	20.2	20.4	21.5	22.2
Diesel fuel	5.7	5.9	6.1	5.9	5.5	5.7	6.2	6.8	7.1	7.9	8.5
Burning oil (Kerosene)	2.6	2.6	2.7	2.1	1.9	1.7	1.7	1.7	1.9	2.0	2.0
Gas oil	12.6	12.3	12.4	10.6	10.0	9.5	9.0	8.9	8.7	8.3	7.7
Fuel oil:											
Power stations	10.2	11.1	10.7	6.3	4.8	6.3	3.8	19.8	9.5	5.6	4.4
Other uses	17.1	16.9	16.3	12.7	10.8	9.9	8.7	8.0	6.4	7.0	5.4
Refinery fuel	6.4	6.4	6.5	6.3	5.4	5.5	5.3	5.4	5.2	5.4	5.2
Gaseous Fuels					*Million therms*						
Liquified petroleum gas[5]	629	633	690	600	564	685	833	912	731	888	905
Other petroleum gas[5]	115	93	153	139	125	302	379	489	535	680	733
Coke oven gas[6]	903	780	831	619	578	537	544	438	604	587	611
Blast furnace gas	770	686	775	352	503	442	481	486	517	576	573
Town gas	70	32	36	31	27	23	18	17	16	14	11
Natural gas[7]	14,803	15,636	17,067	17,278	17,385	17,594	17,954	18,529	19,806	20,047	20,774

1 Includes only those fuels which are sources of air pollution. Source: Warren Spring Laboratory, Department of Trade and Industry using the Digest of United Kingdom Energy. Statistics published by the Department of Energy

2 Final energy users (ie industry other than fuel conversion industries), and also includes public services, railways, agriculture and miscellaneous.

3 Includes low temperature carbonisation and patent fuel plants.

4 Includes public services, railways, agriculture and miscellaneous.

5 Excludes gas already included under "Refinery fuel" which is a mixture of gas and oil fuel.

6 Unpurified.

7 Includes substitute natural gas.

Note: 1 million therms is approximately equivalent to 4,000 tonnes mixture of gas and oil fuel. of coal or 2,400 tonnes of petroleum.

OECD, (1982) Long term projection of the world automobile industry, Paris.

TANNER, J C, (1983) International comparisons of cars and car usage. TRRL Report 1070, Transport and Road Research Laboratory, Crowthorne.

UNITED NATIONS, (1986) Annual bulletin of transport statistics for Europe.

WATKINS, L H, (1981) Environmental impact of roads and traffic: Applied Science Publishers.

WHEATON, W, (1982) The longrun structure of transportation and gasoline demand. International Automobile Program.

2 Exhaust emissions and their measurement

2.1 The pollutants

Figure 2.1, reproduced from a review of air-borne pollutants produced by vehicle exhausts written by Sherwood and Bowers (1970), shows how they are emitted from the vehicle into the atmosphere. A significant proportion of the hydrocarbons comes from the fuel tank, the carburettor and the crank-case, but the exhaust gases are the major source of pollutants. In addition to these air-borne pollutants there is a quantity of dust produced from the gradual wearing away of the rubber tyres, brake linings and clutch plates of the vehicle. We shall, however, not be concerned with this in the present review.

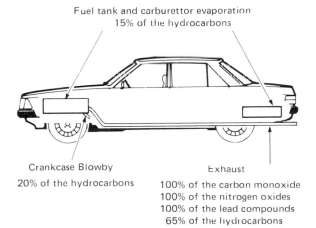

Fuel tank and carburettor evaporation
15% of the hydrocarbons

Crankcase Blowby
20% of the hydrocarbons

Exhaust
100% of the carbon monoxide
100% of the nitrogen oxides
100% of the lead compounds
65% of the hydrocarbons

Fig 2.1   Pattern of emissions from an uncontrolled vehicle

If combustion and oxidation were complete in the engine, water and carbon dioxide would be the only products of the combustion of fuel. Some years ago it would have been possible to assert that neither of these is a pollutant; however although we can still assume that this is true about the water it cannot be taken for granted about carbon dioxide. This will be discussed further in later chapters.

In practice complete oxidation is impossible to achieve, and carbon monoxide is formed in considerable quantities. Some fuel is emitted unchanged, and some is converted into other organic compounds. Apart from these products of incomplete combustion many petrols contain 'anti-knock' agents that contain lead, and lead compounds are therefore found in the exhaust. Sulphur dioxide in the atmosphere is primarily the product of power stations and other industrial processes, and is not an important aspect of road traffic pollution, but in densely trafficked areas the concentrations emitted by vehicles, mainly diesels, may require consideration. In addition the conditions in the combustion chamber favour the oxidation of the nitrogen in the air so that oxides of nitrogen are also formed. To summarise, the following compounds are present in the exhaust gases:

Water vapour: Not considered to be a pollutant
Carbon dioxide: Not previously considered as a pollutant
Carbon monoxide
Oxides of nitrogen
Lead compounds
Hydrocarbons
Sulphur dioxide
Carbon particles (smoke)

The smoke listed is produced in the form of very fine particles of carbon also resulting from incomplete combustion, which acts as a nucleus for other materials, usually in diesel engines. This smoke is the only item that is always clearly visible and for that reason gives rise to much comment from the public.

Under some circumstances the products emitted by vehicles can react with each other to produce unpleasant secondary products. This is now a global problem, although an area where it was first recognised was in Los Angeles where because of the bright sunlight and the peculiar topography of the region the oxides of nitrogen and some of the hydrocarbons react photochemically to form the notorious 'smog'. Odour is also a problem, particularly with diesel engines. The unburnt fuel itself has an odour generally thought to be unpleasant, and high concentrations of aromatic compounds and oxygenates are formed in the pre-ignition zones of the engines. Some will be subsequently consumed in the high temperature flame zones, but some will be discharged into the atmosphere.

In the next sections of this Chapter methods of measurement are discussed, and it is important to realise at the outset that these are for two different but complementary purposes. One is to measure the quality of the air we breathe with all the component parts mixed and dispersed, and the other is to measure directly the component parts as they emerge from vehicle exhausts.

2.2 Methods of measurement - in the field

2.2.1 The TRRL mobile laboratory

In order to measure air pollution in the field it is common to make use of some form of mobile laboratory, and a typical one (Figure 2.2) has been employed for about 15 years at the UK Transport and Road Research Laboratory (Bevan and Hickman, 1974).

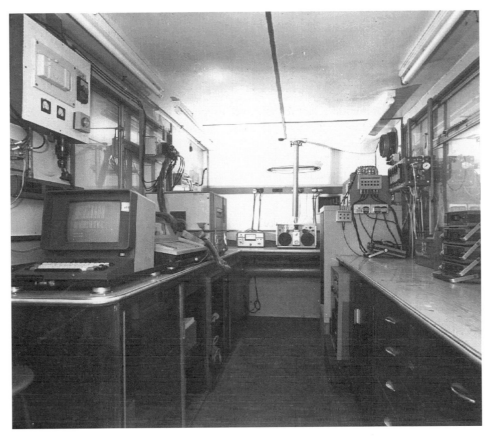

Fig 2.2   The TRRL mobile laboratory for monitoring air pollution

Although the apparatus in this has been up-dated over the years it has remained similar in principle, and a more up-to-date description of it was given in 1988 by the Middlesex Polytechnic. It is equipped to monitor atmospheric carbon monoxide, nitric oxide, nitrogen dioxide, sulphur dioxide, ozone, gaseous hydrocarbons (comprising methane, nonmethane and total), and total particulates. Particulate samples are subsequently tested for both lead and selected polycyclic-aromatic hydrocarbons.

The laboratory requires a mains voltage electrical supply, which can be provided by a portable generator (being careful that the exhaust emissions from this are not taken up by the sampling system of the laboratory). Also carried are gas cylinders, a hydrogen generator, an air purification system, and sample pumps.

The instruments are summarised in Table 2.1, and can be divided into five main categories:

1.   Those used to monitor specific pollutants, both gaseous and particulate.
2.   Those used to monitor meteorological parameters.
3.   Those used to collect and store traffic data.
4.   Those used in calibration.
5.   The computer.

7

TABLE 2.1

Pollutant analysers installed in the mobile laboratory

Pollutant	Detection principle
Carbon monoxide	In laboratory: Infra red
	Portable detector: Electrochemical
Oxides of nitrogen	Chemiluminescence
Sulphur dioxide	U V fluorescence
Total and nonmethane hydrocarbons	Flame ionisation
Ozone	U V absorption
Total suspended particulates	Beta attenuation gravimetric

A diagram of the gas handling system is shown in Figure 2.3.

2.2.2   Carbon monoxide

Carbon monoxide (CO) is monitored continuously using an infra-red gas correlation analyser.

The main components of gas filter correlation spectrometry are shown in Figure 2.4. Initially infra-red radiation is passed through a rotating gas filter containing two partitioned gases, nitrogen and carbon monoxide (Klein and Gourdon, 1982). The radiation is then passed into the sample cell through a bandpass filter. Sample air is drawn through the sample cell, where infra-red radiation is absorbed by some components of the air. The infra-red radiation then leaves the sample cell and is directed towards a pre-amplifier and a detector.

The high concentration of CO gas in one half of the rotating filter produces a reference beam which cannot be further attenuated by any CO in the sample cell. The nitrogen filter is, however, transparent to those frequencies which are absorbed by CO and thus radiation passing through this half of the filter can be further attenuated by CO in the

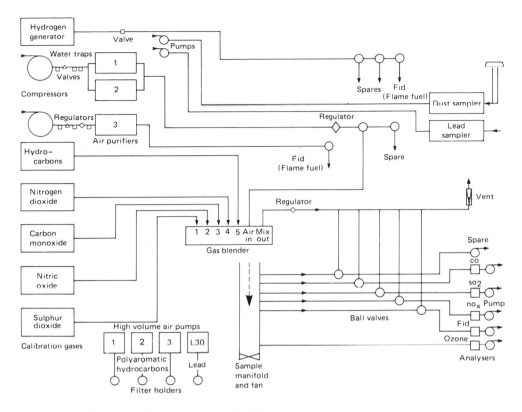

Fig 2.3   The TRRL mobile laboratory gas handling system

sample. Other gases in the sample absorb both the reference and sample beams equally. High sensitivity is possible by using a long path length within the sample cell. As a result, full scale sensitivity can be down to 1 ppm with a lower detectable limit of 0.02 ppm.

During an air pollution survey, CO is commonly measured at a number of nearby locations in addition to the mobile laboratory sites. Portable battery-operated electrochemical analysers are used, housed in strong, lockable boxes. The electrochemical sensor has a platinum anode at which CO is oxidised to CO_2, while hydrogen ions from water in the sensor cell are liberated at a cathode, according to the reaction:

$$CO + H_2O = CO_2 + 2H^* + 2e$$

The current generated by this sensor is proportional to the concentration of the CO within the sample.

The instrument can operate continuously for up to eight hours using its internal batteries. With an additional external battery, wired in parallel with the pump battery unit, the analyser can operate for at least 24 hours before needing recharging.

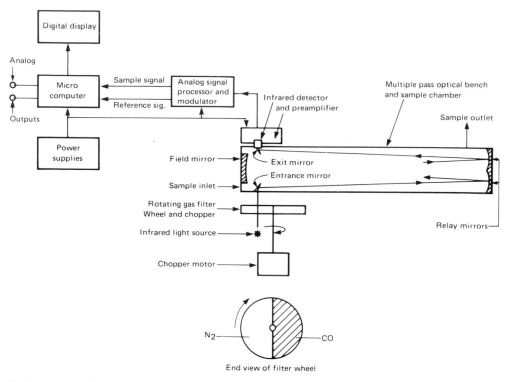

Fig 2.4   A gas filter correlation Infra-Red spectrophotometer

This instrument is fairly specific to CO, but minor interferences can arise in atmospheres with either high acetylene or ethylene levels.

For ambient monitoring purposes a range of 0 to 50 ppm is commonly used. The analyser has a minimum detectable sensitivity of 0.5 per cent of full scale with a rise time of 25 seconds. Data are continuously logged onto compact data loggers. At the end of a sampling period data are transferred onto the minicomputer in the mobile laboratory and stored on either data cartridge or flexible disc.

2.2.3   Oxides of nitrogen

Nitrogen oxides are monitored using a chemiluminescence analyser. The principle of the instrument is based on the chemiluminescence of nitrogen dioxide in a raised-energy atomic state as a result of the reaction between nitric oxide (NO) and ozone (O_3):

$$NO + O_3 \longrightarrow NO_2{}^* + O_2$$

As the activated NO_2^* reverts back to a lower energy state it emits radiation (Perry and Hutchinson, 1986) that is detected by a photomultiplier tube. The current produced in the photomultiplier is directly proportional to the radiation intensity and thus to the NO concentration in the sample.

10

The instrument is of dual channel design and comprises two complete detection systems where nitric oxide and total oxides of nitrogen are measured separately. The chemiluminescence technique measures only nitric oxide. Thus NO is measured directly while total oxides of nitrogen are measured by passing the sample stream through a converter where the NO_2 fraction of the sample is reduced to NO prior to entry into the reaction chamber. Nitrogen dioxide is subsequently calculated internally by the subtraction of the results from the two channels. A possible error in the NO_x readings can be caused by the conversion of species such as nitro-PAHs, ammonia, organic nitrates, nitric and nitrous acids to NO.

The analyser has a minimum detectable concentration of 2.0 ppb, with a fall and rise time of three minutes.

2.2.4 Sulphur dioxide

Sulphur dioxide is measured using a fluorescence analyser. This instrument operates by ultraviolet excitation of SO_2 molecules, which produces a fluorescent output proportional to pollutant concentration (Ferrari *et al.*, 1977). Sample gas is passed into a reaction chamber where it is subjected to a beam of mechanically chopped UV radiation. The resulting fluorescence is detected by a photomultiplier tube.

The analyser has a lower detection limit of 1.0 ppb with a minimum response time (rise and fall) of four minutes.

2.2.5 Ozone

Ozone is measured using an analyser based on the absorption, by ozone, of UV light at a wavelength of 254 nm. The instrument operates with dual channels which differ in that one channel incorporates an ozone scrubber to remove completely all traces of ozone. Thus comparative measurements are obtained between the UV absorption of the ozone free air and the ozone contaminated sample.

Photomultiplier tubes are used to monitor the amount of absorption and the difference between the two channels is expressed as a voltage output which can be related, by the Beer-Lambert law, to the concentration of ozone.

2.2.6 Hydrocarbons

Gaseous hydrocarbons are monitored using a flame ionisation detector. This operates continuously, providing outputs for methane and total hydrocarbons, with a value for nonmethane (reactive) hydrocarbons calculated internally by the subtraction of these two measured channels. The sample gas is passed into a polarised hydrogen flame where, upon combustion, compounds with carbon-hydrogen bonds form ions. A potential difference applied between the flame and collector electrodes results in a migration of these ions which can be detected as an electric current. This ion current is proportional to the concentration of hydrocarbons in the sample.

The hydrocarbon analyser incorporates a scrubber, in the form of an activated carbon precolumn, which is periodically switched into the sample stream in order to remove all hydrocarbons other than methane. While the unit is measuring total hydrocarbons the carbon scrubber is switched out of the gas stream, and it is backflushed to remove the collected hydrocarbons. Very light hydrocarbons such as acetylene and ethylene can pass through the scrubber, thus interfering with the analysis and causing the amount of methane to be overestimated.

2.2.7   Total suspended particulates

Suspended solids are filtered from air samples taken into the mobile laboratory through a mast protruding through the roof. The mast is heated to prevent condensation on the pipe walls and has an omnidirectional stainless steel sampling head. The air sample ultimately passes through a glass fibre paper roll where the suspended particulates are collected as 1 cm^2 spots.

The mass of collected particles is measured by their attenuation of beta radiation. Attenuation has little dependence on the physiochemical composition of the dust. A Geiger Mueller tube is used as the detector for the beta radiation which is produced by a promethium 147 source.

Concentrations can be measured for periods between 0.5 and 24 hours. Suspended solids accumulate on the filter paper during each period, after which the filter is exposed to the beta radiation. The attenuation produced by the sample compared with that of the clean filter paper is determined and displayed as a voltage output proportional to the mass of particles deposited on the filter.At the end of each accumulation and measurement period the filter paper is advanced and the cycle repeated.

Initial instrument calibration is undertaken by the manufacturer and is not user adjustable. A calibration check is provided in the form of a standard foil which can be placed between the radiation source and the receiver.

 Total suspended solids are also collected on 60 mm diameter glass fibre filter papers using a high volume sampling pump. The filter papers are initially heated to constant weight, weighed and then exposed for 24 hours. At the end of this period they are again dried and the gain in weight is measured. The filter papers are also analysed for lead content.

2.2.8   Particulate lead

Samples for lead analysis are collected by drawing air through a tape sampler, using glass fibre filter material. Sampling times on this particular equipment can be selected from four fixed periods between 1 and 24 hours. The main laboratory sampling manifold is not used for the lead sample because of the possibility of deposition within the long sample lines. Instead, a half metre length of 0.25 inch PTFE tubing is used.

The samples are analysed for lead using standard atomic absorption spectrophotometric techniques.

2.2.9 Polycyclic aromatic hydrocarbons

To obtain large enough samples for the analysis, additional particulate samples are collected using high volume pumps and glass fibre filters. The aluminium open faced filter holders are mounted on the side of the mobile laboratory, and covered by a canopy to keep the filters dry and out of direct sunlight.

Sampling times are set at eight hourly intervals, controlled by the mobile laboratory's minicomputer. The computer switches the three pumps on and off in turn, giving three samples daily. The hydrocarbons are liberated from the particulates trapped on the filter paper using ultrasonic agitation in dichloromethane (CH_2Cl_2). The samples are analysed for PAH, using a mass spectrometer after separation by capillary gas chromatographs.

2.2.10 Meteorological data

The mobile unit is equipped to monitor several meteorological parameters including wind speed and direction, air temperature and relative humidity. All four of these parameters are logged continuously by the computer. Standard apparatus is used for this purpose, and wherever necessary supplementary data are obtained from the nearest Meteorological Office weather station.

2.2.11 Traffic flow data

Traffic volumes can be monitored using pressure loops set across the road surface. These count total axle numbers, which can be related to vehicle flow. These loops can operate either using portable roadside loggers or connected directly onto the mobile laboratory computer. At some sites counts are available from traffic induction loops in the road surface.

Vehicle speed is important as it influences the pollutant emission rates, but to the present date there are no routinely used techniques for average speed determination, in connection with roadside air pollution monitoring stations. Speed limits provide clues as to actual speeds, and both manual and automatic methods have been used for timing vehicles over measured sections of road. In the future one might see more use of radar gun devices to monitor the speeds of representative samples of vehicles, and perhaps the introduction of road surface induction loops in pairs.

2.2.12 Calibration facility

Before and after any survey, all the equipment in the mobile laboratory requires calibration for zero, span and linearity. During a survey the gaseous analysers require zero and span checking approximately twice a week, with the exception of the portable CO analysers which require daily calibration checks.

For comparators, single concentration gases (nitric oxide, nitrogen dioxide, sulphur dioxide, carbon monoxide and a hydrocarbon mixture) are used with a gas blender to provide a range of concentrations. Air for instrument zero adjustment and gas dilution processes is produced using air purifiers that oxidise all combustible compounds including methane to carbon dioxide and water vapour through the action of a high temperature platinum catalyst. Water vapour and nitrogen oxides are removed by an inbuilt molecular sieve.

A compressor is connected to the air purifiers providing a relatively inexpensive source of pure air.

2.2.13 Data acquisition

The mobile laboratory has a minicomputer with an eight inch double disc drive, data cartridge recorder, printer and visual display unit. The computer can accept analogue and digital input channels and can also provide a range of output signals for controlling parts of the monitoring equipment.

The data logging program operated by the computer monitors the voltage outputs from each analyser every second excluding the lead tape sampler and high volume pumps. It converts the voltage outputs to the appropriate units, and calculates ten minute averages that are stored on flexible disc.

Hourly average concentrations are also calculated and are recorded on the printer. At the end of each 24 hour period, a set of tabulated data is printed indicating the average concentrations over two sampling periods (0700-1900 and 0000 - 2400), the four highest concentrations over the 24 hour period, and the time over which a set concentration limit has been exceeded. A sample printout is shown in Table 2.2.

2.3 Methods of measurement - laboratory facility

The facility described in the previous section enables air quality to be measured on the road, and airborne concentrations of the various pollutants produced by vehicles to be detected and quantified. It is necessary to have corresponding equipment for measuring exhaust emission rates during research and development, and for type testing of production vehicles so that legislative limits can be met and improvements made. Provided that this is done effectively it seems likely that with the increasing sophistication

Table 2.2

A sample printout from the TRRL mobile laboratory

RESULTS FROM 31-OCT-86
HOURLY AVERAGES

TIME	CO (PPM)	NO (PPHM)	NO2 (PPHM)	NOx (PPHM)	O3 (PPHM)	SO2 (PPHM)	THC (PPM)	CH4 (PPM)	NMHC (PPM)	DUST (VOLT)	WD (CPTS)	WS (M/S)	TEMP (DEGAC)	RHUM (%)
0	1.056	28.80	1.919	30.71	0.248	1.927	2.390	2.386	0.288	******	644454	1.578	10.76	65.08
1	0.747	19.64	1.863	21.49	0.264	1.989	2.319	2.363	0.218	******	444445	1.388	11.12	63.31
2	0.501	16.80	1.643	18.44	0.277	2.024	2.299	2.361	0.199	******	444444	1.437	11.13	67.08
3	0.324	10.70	1.333	12.03	0.346	2.118	2.260	2.359	0.164	******	454444	0.893	11.76	67.61
4	0.509	17.78	1.608	19.33	0.296	2.210	2.273	2.360	0.177	******	444544	1.782	11.96	67.32
5	0.598	28.28	2.124	30.40	0.339	2.158	2.339	2.361	0.240	******	444444	2.843	12.15	65.09
6	1.316	58.86	2.680	61.53	0.446	1.964	2.475	2.390	0.345	******	454444	3.803	12.24	62.81
7	3.710	112.1	2.982	115.1	0.600	1.701	3.054	2.543	0.778	******	444444	4.732	12.53	62.91
8	3.986	116.3	2.951	119.2	0.579	1.614	3.099	2.534	0.829	******	444544	4.934	12.99	60.83
9	3.593	102.4	3.367	105.8	0.614	1.640	2.892	2.492	0.660	******	444444	5.051	13.72	58.33
10	2.929	93.73	3.476	97.20	0.605	1.826	2.512	2.512	0.551	******	444454	4.847	15.02	57.34
11	2.888	89.97	3.442	93.41	0.573	2.077	2.699	2.391	0.573	******	444444	5.020	16.09	54.93
12	2.736	84.27	3.772	88.02	0.624	2.474	2.542	2.370	0.448	******	444445	4.484	16.56	53.25
13	2.929	87.50	3.916	91.41	0.614	2.396	2.738	2.368	0.637	******	444444	4.688	16.35	53.80
14	3.123	93.42	3.657	97.08	0.587	1.478	2.821	2.366	0.712	******	444444	5.404	16.01	53.27
15	3.525	95.40	3.477	98.87	0.590	1.010	2.912	2.387	0.804	******	444445	5.449	15.73	54.36
16	4.382	79.59	3.402	82.98	0.546	0.816	3.181	2.450	1.008	******	443444	3.439	14.81	62.24
17	6.670	63.13	3.603	66.72	0.498	1.830	3.615	2.466	1.434	******	444445	2.691	14.73	66.74
18	5.600	35.75	3.296	39.03	0.472	2.310	3.050	2.542	0.790	******	444444	1.932	14.62	72.22
19	4.451	76.70	3.212	79.89	0.368	2.300	3.028	2.486	0.817	******	444444	3.816	14.30	73.47
20	2.823	68.12	2.864	70.97	0.282	2.111	2.598	2.390	0.484	******	444445	4.333	14.89	73.26
21	1.886	48.97	2.323	51.27	0.228	2.243	2.469	2.379	0.367	******	444444	3.538	15.28	76.69
22	1.386	35.24	1.918	37.15	0.231	2.434	2.347	2.372	0.245	******	444444	3.104	15.44	78.90
23	1.441	32.29	1.961	34.24	0.249	2.596	2.306	2.299	0.280	******	444444	3.295	15.81	78.33

AVERAGE MEASUREMENTS

TIME	CO (PPM)	NO (PPHM)	NO2 (PPHM)	NOx (PPHM)	O3 (PPHM)	SO2 (PPHM)	THC (PPM)	CH4 (PPM)	NMHC (PPM)	DUST (VOLT)	WD (CPTS)	WS (M/S)	TEMP (DEGAC)	RHUM (%)
7-19	3.839	87.80	3.445	91.24	0.575	1.764	2.950	2.452	0.769			4.394	14.93	59.23
0-24	2.630	62.32	2.783	65.10	0.436	1.968	2.688	2.414	0.544			3.522	14.02	64.66

MAXIMUM CONCENTRATIONS

	CO (PPM)	NO (PPHM)	NO2 (PPHM)	NOx (PPHM)	O3 (PPHM)	SO2 (PPHM)	THC (PPM)	CH4 (PPM)	NMHC (PPM)	DUST (VOLT)	WD (CPTS)	WS (M/S)	TEMP (DEGC)	RHUM (%)
TIME	17.40	8.10	13.50	8.10	7.10	23.40	17.40	18.20	17.40	0.00		15.20	12.00	23.00
VALUE	9.323	126.9	4.191	129.8	0.725	2.659	4.532	2.631	2.344	******		6.132	16.79	79.53
TIME	17.50	7.30	17.40	7.30	12.50	23.30	16.40	7.30	16.40	0.10		14.50	11.50	22.40
VALUE	7.403	122.2	4.107	125.3	0.713	2.620	3.681	2.564	1.485	******		5.722	16.77	79.31
TIME	19.00	7.50	12.50	7.50	9.30	23.50	17.00	7.20	17.00	0.20		11.00	12.40	22.50
VALUE	6.996	122.2	4.079	125.2	0.693	2.618	3.652	2.559	1.461	******		5.555	16.60	79.13
TIME	18.50	8.00	13.00	8.00	14.50	13.30	19.00	8.10	17.30	0.30		14.30	12.10	23.20
VALUE	6.266	121.8	3.939	124.6	0.689	2.614	3.634	2.559	1.420	******		5.555	16.58	79.11

TIME ABOVE SET LIMITS

	CO (PPM)	NO (PPHM)	NO2 (PPHM)	NOx (PPHM)	O3 (PPHM)	SO2 (PPHM)	THC (PPM)	CH4 (PPM)	NMHC (PPM)	DUST (VOLT)	WD (CPTS)	WS (M/S)	TEMP (DEGC)	RHUM (%)
LEVEL	50.00	200.0	200.0	200.0	50.00	10000	20.00	20.00	20.00	10000.		10000.	10000.	10000.
TIME	0.00	0.00	0.00	0.00	0.00	0.00	0.00	0.00	0.00	-0.01		0.00	0.00	0.00

Index:

THC = total hydrocarbon
NMHC = non-methane hydrocarbon
WD = wind direction (each digit is a sector numbered out of 8, as a ten-minute reading)
WS = wind speed
RHUM = relative humidity

of modern engines, electronic ignition and so on the type-tested engine will be able to maintain its emission ratings with only normal servicing and simple garage testing.

Such laboratory installations are maintained by many large-scale manufacturers and others. What follows is taken from a description kindly provided by Ricardo Consulting Engineers of their equipment at Shoreham, West Sussex in the UK.

2.3.1   Chassis dynamometer

For testing on a dynamometer engines are divided into two categories, determined by the gross vehicle weight (GVW) of the vehicle in which the engine will operate. Vehicles having a GVW of less than 3500 kg in Europe, 6000 lbs (2700 kg) and an option up to 8500 lbs (3600 kg) in the USA and 2500 kg in Japan are called "light duty" and the engine is tested in the vehicle on a chassis dynamometer. Vehicles over these GVWs are classed as "heavy duty" and it is usual to perform the engine emissions tests with the engine running on a test bed installation. "Light duty" includes both diesel and petrol engined passenger cars, small delivery vans, light trucks, light commercial vehicles, and motorcycles.

A car on a chassis dynamometer is shown in Figure 2.5. It is not necessary here to describe the dynamometer in great detail. Ambient air temperature is controlled, and so is vehicle temperature, and variations in humidity and barometric pressure are measured and corrected for. The purpose of the dynamometer is then to be able to "drive" the vehicle to a standard cycle of starting, idling, accelerating and decelerating, making use of either a water brake power absorption unit (PAU), a DC motor to absorb and supply power, or a DC motor with additional capacity to simulate vehicle inertia electronically. Calibration of the dynamometer is essential over the speed range covered by the test cycle, and requires considerable expertise. Repeatability of values of speed of $\pm$ 0.5 per cent is possible when using DC dynamometers and about $\pm$ 2.5 per cent with water brake equipment.

Fig 2.5   Emissions testing of a light duty vehicle on a chassis dynamometer

16

2.3.2 Exhaust gas sampling

The nature of the sampling and of subsequent testing depends to an extent upon the regulations that are required to be met by the emissions, and these will be discussed in detail in the following chapter, although it is useful here to show (Fig 2.6) the drive cycles used at present for the major areas of the world that require emissions testing.

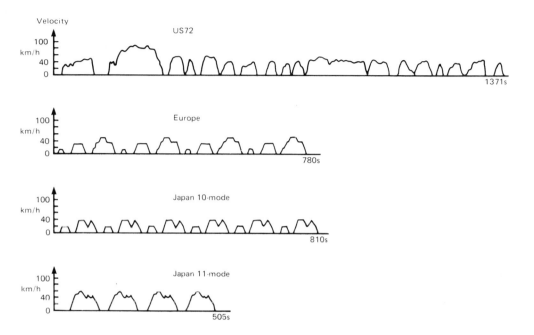

Fig 2.6   Comparison of national driving cycles

For Europe and Japan the drive cycles require the vehicles to perform relatively simple acceleration and deceleration patterns which are repeated to give a drive of four cycles for the European and Japanese (11 Mode) cold start tests and six cycles for the Japanese hot start test (10 Mode). The European and the two Japanese cycles are each of different patterns. For the USA, however, there is a more complex driving pattern to be performed from a cold start. The drive cycle includes differing speed and acceleration loops and part of the cycle is repeated from a hot start condition (not shown in the Figure). The cold and hot start phases of the test are weighted before combining with the "stabilised" section to give an overall test result.

Figure 2.7 shows the European cycle to a larger scale, including the gear positions. Figure 2.8 shows the high speed cycle that is to be added to the present cycle since this is based only upon urban driving practice. This is an obvious requirement. Attempts to establish a harmonised drive cycle for use worldwide have so far met with little success, although there would clearly be much advantage in doing so.

After installation on the chassis dynamometer the vehicle exhaust is connected to the exhaust gas sampler which conditions the exhaust gas before storing all or part of the

17

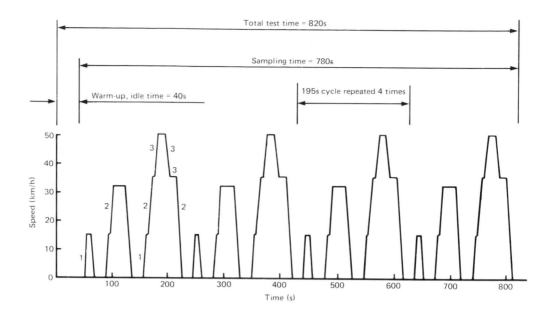

Fig 2.7   European ECE R 15 driving cycle to larger scale

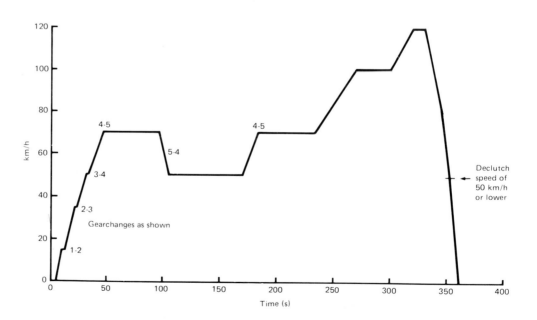

Fig 2.8   'Extra Urban' high speed driving cycle

18

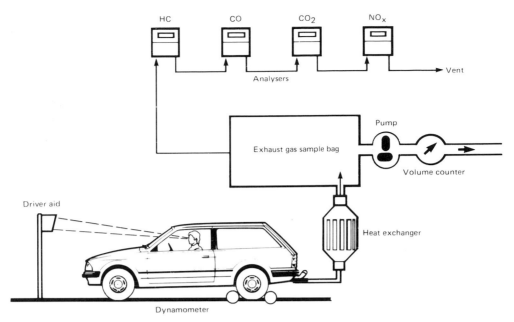

Fig 2.9   Exhaust gas sampling system (-European-15-03) the 'big bag' system
          (Provided by Ricardo Consulting Engineers)

sample. The exhaust gas is analysed at the end of the test for the main pollutants, namely unburnt hydrocarbons, carbon monoxide and oxides of nitrogen.

The old procedure for Europe (Fig 2.9) employed a large condensing chamber through which the total exhaust gas from the vehicle was passed in order to dry the gas before storing the raw gas sample in large plastic, "Tedlar", sample bags. This "big bag" system was not suitable for use with diesel engined vehicles due to the rapid pollution of the bag with diesel particulates and condensed hydrocarbons. The size or number of the big bags was indirectly related to the engine capacity and/or overall gearing of the vehicle.

The "big bag" system was replaced in Europe by the "Constant Volume Sampling" system (CVS) as the recommended method of first conditioning and then storing the gas sample over the drive cycle. The CVS system has been used for the last decade in the USA for the measurement of exhaust emissions from light duty diesel and gasoline engined vehicles.

There are two main types of CVS unit, the positive displacement pump (PDP) and the critical flow venturi (CFV), but both use the same basic principle of diluting the exhaust gas with air to produce a constant volume of diluted exhaust gas over the drive cycle. From the main diluted stream of exhaust gas a small sample is taken at a constant flow rate to a small (1m square) sample bag. The sample bag contents and those of an ambient air sample bag are analysed at the end of the test. The ambient air sample is used to correct the vehicle sample for the ambient pollutant levels.

19

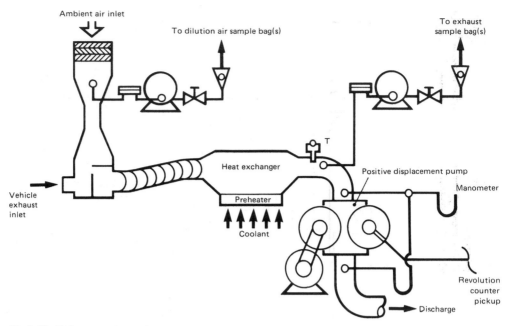

Fig 2.10 Exhaust gas sampling using the Positive Preplacement Pump-Constant Volume Sampling System (PDP-CVS)
(Provided by Ricardo Consulting Engineers)

The PDP - CVS system (Fig 2.10) employs a positive displacement pump as the main gas mover and the speed of this pump may be adjusted for the vehicle under test so that the mean diluted carbon dioxide level over the drive cycle is less than 3 per cent carbon dioxide. Under these conditions there is sufficient dilution of the exhaust gas to prevent any problems due to water vapour in the analytical system.

A heat exchanger is used ahead of the PDP in order to control the temperature of the dilute exhaust gas entering the PDP to within ± 5°C of a set point ie to control the total gas throughput to within ± 2 per cent.

With the CFV system, shown in Fig 2.11, a venturi is made to operate at critical flow conditions by placing the venturi upstream of a large air pump. It may be shown that under critical flow conditions the venturi flow is inversely proportional to temperature and it follows therefore that the rate of flow through the CFV is inherently less temperature sensitive than the PDP system. If a small CFV unit is used to extract the sample from the main gas stream and supply this to the sample bag then proportional sampling is achieved without the use of a heat exchanger.

The CVS systems are calibrated for flow rate over a range of operating conditions by the use of standard air flow meters of the viscous flow, turbine meter or venturi flow meter types affixed to the entry duct of the CVS unit under calibration (Fig 2.12). Additionally a tracer gas technique either in the form of gravimetric or volumetric dosing of propane or carbon monoxide into the main airstream to the CVS may be used to perform an overall system verification. Both the sample collection and analytical systems may be

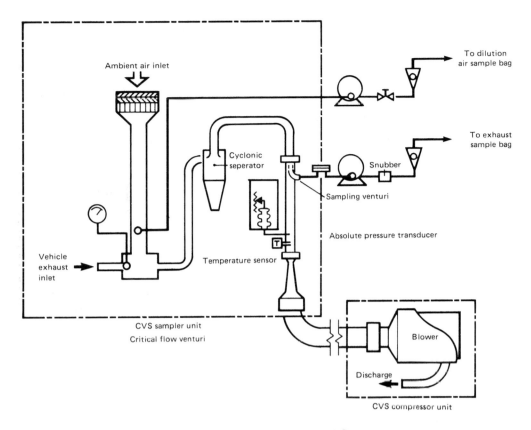

*Fig 2.11 Exhaust gas sampling using the Critical Flow Venturi-Constant
Volume Sampling System
(Provided by Ricardo Consulting Engineers)*

checked by either metering a constant flow of pure gas using a critical flow orifice, or metering a limited quantity of pure gas (carbon monoxide or propane) by means of a gravimetric technique.

2.3.3 Diesel particulate sampling for light vehicles

In the USA and Europe, in addition to the limits set for the emission of hydrocarbon, carbon monoxide and NOx from engines and vehicles there are limits set for the emission of particulates. The particulate emitted by the diesel engine is some 10 to 20 times that of the comparable petrol engine running on unleaded fuel and it is therefore only the diesel engined vehicle that we need to consider here.

The measurement of the diesel exhaust particulate is achieved by use of a particulate development tunnel situated ahead of the CVS unit. The CVS and Particulates Tunnel arrangement for US Federal Testing is shown in Fig 2.13.

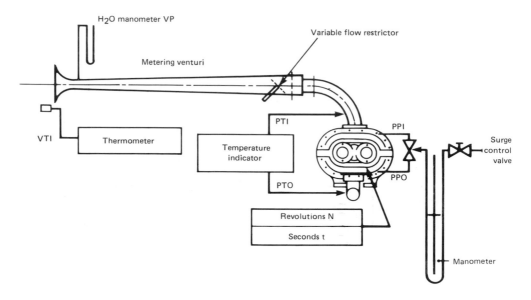

H₂O manometer VP

Variable flow restrictor

Metering venturi

VTI

Thermometer

PTI

PPI

Surge control valve

Temperature indicator

PTO

PPO

Manometer

Revolutions N

Seconds t

Fig 2.12 PDP-CVS calibration configuration
(Provided by Ricardo Consulting Engineers)

2.3.4   Heavy duty engine emissions

Up to 1986 heavy duty engines, ie those normally fitted into vehicles exceeding 3500 kg in Europe, 6000 lb (2700 kg) GVW in the USA and 2500 kg in Japan, were required to perform a sequence of runs at constant speeds on an engine testbed with the exhaust emissions being measured at each set point.

The test procedure for determining the exhaust emissions from heavy duty engines was changed in the USA in 1986 from a steady state test to a transient test cycle. The cycles to be performed cover a series of varying speed and power loops which differ between the petrol and diesel engines but both types are required to perform their respective cycles from a cold and a hot start. During the transient test the exhaust from the engine is assessed for emissions by use of CVS techniques and for the diesel engine a dilution tunnel is included in the CVS system to allow for the measurement of particulates. Fig 2.14 shows the general layout of the sampling system.

In Europe the diesel engine is tested over a 13 mode, steady-state test sequence. Each mode in the test is a specified combination of engine speed and load. The gaseous exhaust emissions are recorded at each point and then weighting factors are applied to each of the modes to provide a combined measure for comparison with the limit values. The Japanese procedure is similar, using six or ten mode tests depending on the carrying capacity of the vehicle. Further details of these legislative tests are given in Chapter 3.

The analytical systems used for either petrol or diesel engine test work are identical, with the heated sample line and heated Flame Ionisation Detector being used for both engine types.

22

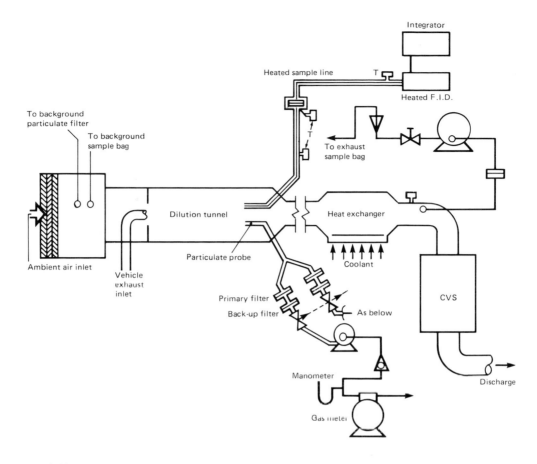

Integrator

Heated sample line

Heated F.I.D.

T

To background particulate filter

To background sample bag

To exhaust sample bag

Dilution tunnel

Heat exchanger

Ambient air inlet

Particulate probe

Vehicle exhaust inlet

Coolant

Primary filter

Back-up filter

As below

CVS

Manometer

Discharge

Gas meter

*Fig 2.13   Particulate and gaseous emissions measurement
(Provided by Ricardo Consulting Engineers)*

2.3.5   The measurement system

A typical system, shown in Fig 2.15, includes all the features required by the US Federal Register for the testing of diesel and gasoline engines over the heavy duty engine emission test procedure. The layout for the analysis system is shown in Fig 2.16. Mobile analysis systems use the same arrangement except for the simplification of excluding the heated sample pump placed at the engine end of the sampling system. These pumps are very expensive and equal results can be obtained by using sample pumps housed either in the analysers themselves, as for the HFID and chemiluminescent NOx analysers, or within the analysis system itself to supply sample gas to the NDIR analysers measuring carbon monoxide and carbon dioxide. The large heated pump systems are reserved for certification work and the use of such a system does prevent errors in analysis resulting from minor leaks in the sample handling system. However, each of the mobile systems has a leakage detection system to enable small leaks to be detected and eliminated.

23

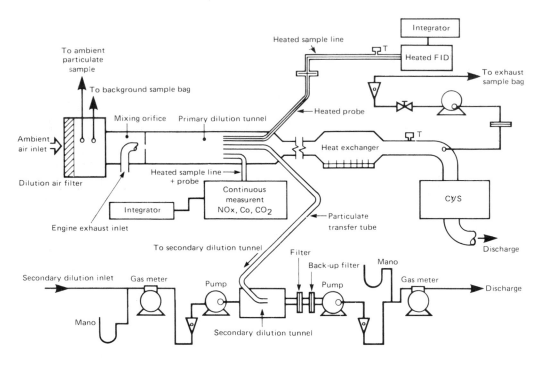

Fig 2.14 Double dilution particulate measurement system
(Provided by Ricardo Consulting Engineers)

With this type of analysis system it is possible to allow for the wide variations in exhaust gas flow rate and temperature when mapping particulate emissions on the load and speed range of an engine. Good repeatability can be obtained for both particulate and gaseous emissions despite the danger of a build-up of hydrocarbons during extended operations at light loads; and it is also possible to collect samples of particulate for further analysis. The system can be used, if required, to monitor optimum levels of exhaust gas recirculation that might be applied to the engine.

2.3.6   Analysis of the sample

Each of the emission tests described requires either continuous analysis of the raw or dilute exhaust gas sample or the analysis of a collected bag sample. The analysis of these samples for the main pollutants, as laid down by current legislation, requires the use of three different analytical techniques before the mass exhaust emission levels may be calculated. Carbon monoxide and carbon dioxide are measured using a non-dispersive infra-red analyser (Section 2.2.2); NOx is measured using a chemiluminescent analyser (Section 2.2.3); hydrocarbons are measured by a flame ionisation process (Section 2.2.6); and particulates are measured using filters and attenuation of beta radiation (Section 2.2.7). Such instruments have already been described in earlier sections dealing with the TRRL mobile laboratory. The particular instruments employed by other organisations might be different in detail, but they serve the same purpose.

Fig 2.15 The Perkins emissions analysis system
(Provided by Perkins Technology Limited)

As is the case with the mobile laboratory, to maintain high standards of accuracy it is necessary to check the performance of the analysers at regular intervals. Several methods of calibrating may be employed but the basic principle remains the same, the instrument being calibrated with an accurately known concentration of gas. Obviously this requires many closely known concentrations of gas, and at least six different points on each range should be checked. It is in the methods used to obtain these closely known mixes that calibration techniques vary.

2.3.7   Emission levels

By establishing the percentage of the pollutant gas and the total volume of exhaust emitted either over the test cycle, the theoretical distance covered, or the sample time, the mass emission levels may be calculated by use of the relative density or molecular weight of the individual pollutant gases. The calculated mass emissions may then be compared with the legislative limits.

For steady state test work on testbed installations the pollutant mass is calculated from the following:

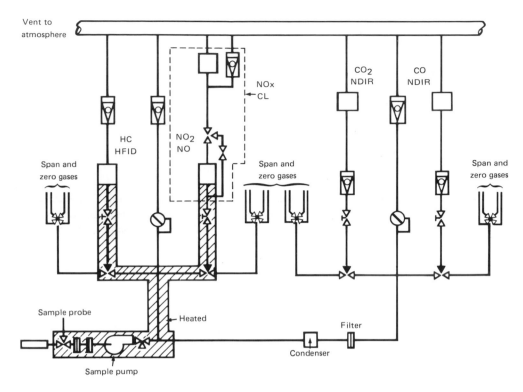

Fig 2.16 *Heavy-duty engine exhaust gas analysis system*
(Provided by Ricardo Consulting Engineers)

$$M = W \times C \times E$$

where   M = mass of pollutant
C = concentration of pollutant
W = molecular weight of pollutant
E = exhaust mass

For diluted exhaust measurements using the CVS testing technique, the mass emissions of the pollutants are calculated by use of the following formula:-

$$M = V \times Q \times C \times 10^{-6}$$

where   M = mass emission of the pollutant
V = volume of diluted exhaust gas at normal conditions
Q = density of pollutant at normal conditions
C = concentration of pollutant in the dilute exhaust gas expressed in ppm corrected for pollutant concentration in the dilution air

2.3.8 Future developments

The legislators have laid down certain limits for the main pollutants in the exhaust gas of engines and these limits have become gradually more severe as the technical

26

development of the engines and their associated clean up devices has progressed to reduce the emitted levels. The gas analysis methods have also developed over this time and analysers have become more stable and reliable. However, as the regulated emission limits continue to fall, the development of more sophisticated analytical techniques will be required since the dilution ratio used during CVS testing, for example, tends to be fixed by the particulate temperature requirements or the dilution level necessary to avoid condensation problems.

The mass spectrometer may possibly have some advantages to offer at these low emission levels although this will require further development before it is accepted. The smaller transportable mass spectrometers have limited resolution and need the aid of a computer to separate exhaust gas components of similar molecular weight, carbon monoxide and nitrogen for example. The computer package resolves this particular problem by monitoring both the monatomic and diatomic elements of nitrogen. The large fixed site mass spectrometer linked to Fourier transform infra-red analysis will detect most of the regulated and unregulated emissions but the measurement of total hydrocarbon emissions remains a difficult area.

The mass spectrometer could be used for the evaluation of CVS sample bags or for raw trace work and there is the possibility of using an inert tracer gas, Krypton perhaps, to monitor the total gas flow through the engine. This would be used for engines on a testbed or in a vehicle in order to calculate emissions over a transient cycle without the need to dilute the exhaust gas using a CVS or similar sampling device. Although these devices are very expensive at the present time, if viewed as a replacement for a complete analytical package it is possible that with further development they could become the total analysis system for the future.

Laser techniques are also being investigated as a means of measuring the low pollutant levels with greater accuracy.

2.4   Methods of measurement - field/laboratory

A comprehensive equipment has been recently developed by Warren Spring Laboratory which samples exhaust gases and particulates from petrol or diesel engines while the vehicle is travelling, over a wide range of driving and engine operating conditions (Fig 2.17). This incorporates a stainless steel flow splitter unit and a miniature constant volume sampler (Mini-CVS), and the original version was suitable for engine sizes up to 3 litres. Versions have now been built which can be used to measure emissions from diesel engines up to about 11 litres.

An alternative exhaust sampler has been designed and developed by TRRL, particularly for use on heavy duty diesel vehicles though it may be adapted for use on smaller vehicles (Latham and Hickman 1990). The sampler maintains a sampling rate constantly proportional to the total exhaust flow by using an electrical closed loop controller. The flowrates of the sample and the air entering the engine are continuously measured and

Fig 2.17 The Warren Springs Laboratory exhaust sampler

compared. Any deviation of the measured ratio from that required is corrected by an automatic change of pressure in the mixing chamber of the system. The pressure change in turn induces a change in the sample flowrate until the correct ratio is reestablished.

Samples using this system may be collected in bags for later analysis or directed immediately to a set of gas analysers for real-time, continuous analysis. This capability is especially useful in measuring and understanding the detailed relationships between engine and vehicle operating conditions and exhaust emission rates since it is possible to observe rapidly varying emissions rather than the average concentrations determined by bag sampling. Because it was developed for use with diesel engines, it incorporates a filter for particulate sampling and may be used in conjunction with a visible smoke meter.

Whilst not suitable for measuring air quality like the mobile laboratory described earlier, and not as accurate as the laboratory sampling equipment, these neatly span a gap between the two and enable measurement of the actual variation of emissions from vehicles in normal service, so that the implications of particular legislative requirements for overall air quality can be examined. This is of importance now, for example, in studies of how polluted air reacts as it moves to remote locations which experience the effects of acid depositions and ozone.

2.5   Exhaust emission rates

Except for lead, which is confined to petrol, petrol engines and diesel engines produce similar materials in their exhausts, although the relative proportions are very different. The emission rates also vary considerably with the operating mode; ie idling, accelerating, cruising, or decelerating. Table 2.3 shows figures on this point produced in 1966. Although engines have been developed since then and controls have been introduced to meet various standards, and an up-to-date table would have different values, it is still of interest in that it shows in a simple way the variation in emission rate that can occur for different operating modes.

The remainder of this chapter will give some particular characteristics of petrol and diesel engines, followed by a discussion of the emission rates of particular pollutants.

TABLE 2.3

Representative composition of exhaust gases (from Pegg and Ramsden) (concentrations in parts per million by volume)

	Pollutant	Idling	Acceleration	Cruising	Deceleration
Petrol engines	Carbon monoxide	69000	29000	27000	39000
	Hydrocarbons	5300	1600	1000	10000
	Nitrogen oxides	30	1020	650	20
	Aldehydes	30	20	10	290
Diesel engines	Carbon monoxide	Trace	1000	Trace	Trace
	Hydrocarbons	400	200	100	300
	Nitrogen oxides	60	350	240	30
	Aldehydes	10	20	10	30

2.5.1   Petrol engines

Emissions from petrol engines are greatly influenced by the air/fuel ratio of the mixture that is drawn into the engine and subsequently burned in the combustion chamber. The variation of the principal pollutants is shown in Figure 2.18, reproduced from a study (Fellowship of Engineering, 1987) commissioned by the Department of the Environment. The dotted line indicates the stoichiometric ratio of air to fuel which is the exact chemical quantity of air required to burn the fuel completely. Due to the difficulty of perfect mixing in the very short time available, combustion is not quite 100 per cent. On the left of the dotted line there is excess fuel and insufficient oxygen from the air (79 per cent nitrogen and 21 per cent oxygen) and hence HC and CO are relatively high, while for leaner (ie less fuel) settings both these pollutants are reduced but not eliminated. NO, formed in the combustion chamber from the nitrogen and oxygen in the air due to the high temperature of combustion, reaches a maximum at ratios slightly weaker than the stoichiometric A/F ratio. At richer (ie more fuel) A/F ratios there is insufficient oxygen, and as settings are leaned off the temperature of combustion is reduced and less nitrogen and oxygen combine. As the nitric oxide formation increases with the temperature of combustion the control of the ignition point by the spark is critical. Retardation reduces the temperature and hence the NO but unfortunately also reduces the efficiency of combustion with consequent deterioration of fuel consumption. On the right of the dotted line in the figure it can be seen that by weakening the mixture to A/F ratios beyond about 16:1 substantial reductions in NO formation are achieved. It will be appreciated from all this that the accurate control of air/fuel ratio and spark timing is vital for the reduction of pollutants.

Exhaust gas recirculation also helps to reduce the formation of NO in the combustion chamber. This is accomplished by feeding up to 10 per cent of the exhaust gas back into the induction system, which reduces the temperature of combustion. It is an inexpensive

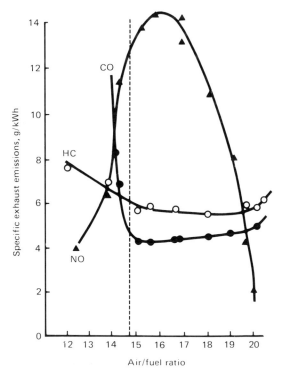

Fig 2.18 Variation of emissions with air/fuel ratio

method but is not universally favoured because of possible contamination of the intake system.

The above are general principles. Current and new techniques (such as lean burn engines and catalysts) will be discussed later in this review.

2.5.2 Diesel engines

Diesel engines offer technical advantages over petrol engines in many ways relevant to pollution. They operate on air/fuel ratios of 20-40:1 or even higher, and are consequently low polluting engines as far as the gaseous pollutants CO, HC and NO_x are concerned. Direct comparisons are difficult but compared with a broadly equivalent petrol engine, CO and HC emissions from diesels can be up to an order of magnitude lower in urban driving conditions with NO_x emissions about one-half to one-third. Fuel economy advantages also exist and can be up to 30-50 per cent better than the broadly equivalent petrol engine in urban driving conditions. At higher power loadings and speeds these differences can be greatly reduced.

However, it is not all advantage for the diesel engines. Particulate emissions arising from incomplete combustion can be a problem for diesels compared with petrol engines especially when the engine is not well maintained.

Diesel fuel also contains roughly ten times as much sulphur as does petrol, so that per unit mass of fuel consumed, SO_2 emissions from diesels are much greater than from petrol engines.

Current diesel engine technologies are conveniently divided into two groups differentiated by the type of combustion chamber. Direct injection (DI) diesel engines are the predominant type in the heavy duty vehicle sector, and here, as the name implies, the fuel is injected directly into a single combustion chamber formed by the cylinder head and piston. The light duty diesel sector employs mostly indirect injection (IDI) where the fuel is injected into a high-swirl pre-chamber containing a glowplug which is used to heat the fuel on cold starting before it passes into the main combustion chamber over the piston.

2.5.3 Carbon monoxide

Road vehicles account for some 85 per cent of total CO emissions in the UK (Department of the Environment, 1988), and most of this comes from petrol engines, the emissions being dependent on the driving mode, and on the state of tune of the engine. Average CO emissions are highest at low speeds (Table 2.4), typically drop to a low point at about 75 km per hour, and increase again at higher speeds.

Increased acceleration rates produce high pollutant emissions in terms of mass per unit time. CO emissions are further increased when petrol engines run below optimum temperature, such as during a cold start when the engine works at low efficiency and

31

TABLE 2.4

Performance-related emission factors as a function of speed (Rogers, 1984)

Speed km per hour	Average emissions CO	g per km HCs	per vehicle NOx
10	33.02	4.47	2.53
25	21.20	2.60	2.17
50	9.80	1.30	2.13
75	6.40	0.93	2.24
100	7.83	0.86	2.97
125	11.04	0.87	4.15
150	13.97	0.92	6.07

is often under choke conditions. Higher CO emissions can thus often be encountered during stop-go driving in urban traffic.

Diesel engines emit only trace levels of CO unless they are poorly maintained, when CO can be emitted with the smoke.

2.5.4   Oxides of nitrogen

NO and NO_2 are both released during combustion, with NO being the major part. They are formed from the oxidation of not only the nitrogen compounds contained in the fuel but also the nitrogen naturally present in the air. Motor vehicles are responsible for about 40 per cent of the total NO_x emissions in the UK, and about 70 per cent of this comes from petrol engines. Under some circumstances, such as during urban driving, motor vehicles can account for up to 70 per cent or even more of concentrations of NO_x at low levels (Williams, 1986).

Average emission rates are at their lowest at speeds of typically 25 to 50 kph (Table 2.4), but rise with increasing speeds. High NO_x emissions are also produced during periods of rapid acceleration.

2.5.5   Hydrocarbons

The pattern of emissions of hydrocarbons from vehicles is very similar to that of CO, with driving mode, engine design and condition being very important. Hydrocarbons are also emitted (Figure 2.1) through evaporation losses from fuel tanks and carburettors, combined with losses from crankcase blow-bys in older engines.

Average gaseous hydrocarbon emissions are typically high at low speeds (Table 2.4), falling to a minimum at about 100 km/h and stabilising at a slightly higher value with further increases in speed. They also increase during rapid acceleration, although as a general rule the highest values are found during idling and deceleration. Diesel engines produce lower hydrocarbon emissions than petrol engines, because of their higher operating efficiency.

2.5.6 Sulphur dioxide

Sulphur dioxide emissions from all classes of motor vehicles are considered negligible, comprising only 1 per cent of the total UK national emissions (Williams, 1986), 46 out of 3,867 thousand tonnes in 1989 although Bennett (Bennett, 1987) suggested in 1987 that 50 per cent of roadside sulphur dioxide concentrations were derived from vehicular emissions. Sulphur emissions from motor vehicles are directly dependent on the sulphur contents of fuels, which are shown in Table 2.5.

TABLE 2.5

Sulphur content of petrol and diesel fuel (per cent/mass)

FUEL	1980	1982	1984	1986
Petrol	0.03	0.06	0.04	0.04
Diesel	0.26	0.23	0.20	0.21

2.5.7 Particulate matter

Atmospheric particulate matter contains a wide variety of solid particles and liquid droplets. This includes a range of substances and materials such as smoke, aerosols formed through atmospheric chemical reactions and metallic compounds (Sherwood and Bowers, 1970). Smoke is defined as suspended particulate air pollutants, with a diameter of less than 15 μm, arising from the incomplete combustion of fossil fuels.

Particles of this size are potentially more dangerous to human health than larger particles, because they remain suspended in air for long periods and can be inhaled.

Concentrations of smoke in the air are measured by determining their soiling capacity. A calibration curve is then used to give concentrations in terms of ''equivalent standard smoke'' per cubic metre of air. In the UK, the annual average urban smoke concentrations fell by about 64 per cent in the ten years from 1967 to 1977, and by 38 per cent from 1977 to 1987.

Motor vehicles are responsible for approximately 40 per cent of the UK national total suspended particulate emissions, predominantly composed of graphitic carbon. Diesel vehicles constitute approximately 10 per cent of the motor traffic in the UK but produce at least 90 per cent of the vehicle generated particulates. The diesel contribution is in contrast to the 1950s and 60s (the final period of the notorious 'London smogs') when most of the elevated smoke and sulphur dioxide concentrations could be credited to coal combustion.

Motor vehicles also generate a range of particulate matter through the dust produced from brakes, clutch plates, tyres and indirectly through the resuspension of particulates on road surfaces through vehicle generated turbulence.

2.5.8   Particulate lead and manganese

The largest source of atmospheric lead, within the United Kingdom, is through the combustion of leaded petrol. Tetra-alkyl-lead compounds are added to petrol as an antiknock agent and also to act as a lubricant within the fuel. Ethylene dibromide and dichloride are further added to the fuel to act as scavengers for lead compounds producing lead bromochlorides. Of the lead compounds added to petrol, approximately 70 per cent are emitted via the exhaust as inorganic salts, about 1 per cent are emitted unchanged as tetra-alkyl-lead compounds and the remainder are trapped in the exhaust system and engine oil (Harrison and Laxen, 1984).

This emission of lead has become so controversial that it seems desirable to explain in some detail the reason for its presence. The Ninth Report of the Royal Commission on Environmental Pollution (1983) published in 1983 gave a good account of this, and the following paragraphs are taken from that report. It should be noted that there have been major changes in the use of lead in UK petrol since the Royal Commission reported. From the beginning of 1986, the maximum lead content was reduced from 0.4 to 0.15 g/l and, in anticipation of the EC requirement that unleaded petrol be available throughout the Community by 1989 (Directive 85/210/EEC), it has been marketed in the UK since 1987. The switch to unleaded petrol was initially slow but, as newer cars designed to use unleaded petrol replace older models, and encouraged by the favourable price difference resulting from changes in excise duty in successive budgets since 1988, sales of unleaded petrol are now a substantial part of the total. This change will be further strengthened by the advent of catalyst-equipped cars from 1993 since they may be operated on unleaded petrol only. Thus, the emission of lead from motor vehicles is rapidly diminishing.

"Acceleration knock occurs at relatively low engine revolutions and is audible when the mechanical engine noise is unobtrusive. However, there is another variety of knock known as high speed knock, which occurs at 4,000-6,000 revolutions per minute. This phenomenon is normally inaudible to the driver above the engine and road noise, but can be measured with special sensors. High speed knock is the most dangerous form because it may occur very rapidly in motorway cruising conditions with the driver unaware until the point where the pistons melt and the engine may seize up.

"An engine's propensity to knock is determined by engineering factors such as the design of the combustion system, the fuel and air mixture preparation, the temperature within the combustion chamber, the engine load and speed; by manufacturing quality; and by the quality and chemical composition of the fuel.

"For a given design of engine, the presence or absence of knock is determined by the combustion quality or 'octane number' of the petrol used. Normally petrol is graded according to the so-called Research Octane Number (RON), but for some purposes the Motor Octane Number (MON) is also important. The higher the RON value, the higher the compression ratio at which the engine can be run without knocking. In the British Standard for petrol (BS 4040) 4 star petrol is a minimum of 97 RON, and in practice varies between 97 and 98.5 RON. With the virtual disappearance of 5 star this is now the highest octane quality generally available in most countries of the world, although some refineries in the Federal Republic of Germany are able to produce values as high as 99.8 RON.

"In the UK some 80 per cent of the present car population requires 4 star petrol for satisfactory operation, at compression ratios typically in the range 9:1-10:1. BS 4040 sets the minimum RON for 3 star (now little used) and 2 star at respectively 94 and 90. Typical compression ratios suitable for 90 RON are between 8:1 and 9:1.

"Octane quality may be increased by intensive refining to increase the proportion of certain hydrocarbons, but this adds to refining costs (and hence to the price of petrol) and produces less petrol from a given quantity of crude oil. Some sixty years ago it was discovered that adding organic lead compounds (lead alkyls) was a convenient and cheap method of boosting the octane quality of petrol. The presence of lead in the fuel has the effect of delaying the abnormal state of partial oxidation in which the end-gas ignites and hence allows engines to operate at higher compression ratios and under greater loads before knocking occurs.

"For a long time, only tetraethyl lead (TEL) was used to increase octane, but in the course of developing petrol with higher octane numbers it was found that for some purposes tetramethyl lead (TML) offered greater advantages, particularly in dealing with acceleration knock. Both TEL and TML are used in current motor fuels.

"The end-gas knocking zone in fact occupies only about 2-10 per cent of the total combustion space, so it follows that only this proportion of the lead actually functions as an anti-knock agent. It is, however, not possible to reduce the lead accordingly and obtain the same results.

"Despite intensive research, to this day no cost-effective alternative to lead as an anti knock additive (as distinct from the use of oxygenates) has been discovered, apart from a manganese compound, methyl cyclopentadienyl manganese tri-carbonyl (MMT), which is a toxic organo-metallic substance converted to a relatively non-toxic oxide (Mn_3O_4) in engine exhaust. MMT is banned in the USA because this oxide clogs up and inactivates catalytic converters. There are also, in the British Government's judgement, sufficient grounds for concern about possible health effects for an assurance to have been obtained from the United

Kingdom Petroleum Industry Association that member companies will not use MMT without prior consultation with the Department of Transport.

''The amount of lead that needs to be added to petrol to bring it up to the required octane number will depend on the quality of the basestock petrol (ie the normal refinery product before the addition of lead), which in turn depends on the amount of additional refining to which it has been subjected in order to increase the proportion of high octane hydrocarbons. There are practical and financial constraints to the amount of octane quality that can be obtained from refining. The upper and lower limits for lead in petrol of 0.4 and 0.15 g/l set by European Community Directive 78/611/EEC represented a compromise between a number of factors applicable to Western Europe generally, notably health objectives, efficient use of energy (both in vehicles and refineries), current engine technology and performance requirements, whilst avoiding obstacles to trade and freedom of movement. Countries which have introduced or plan to introduce unleaded petrol have mostly reduced octane quality rather than incur increasing refinery costs. For practical purposes 0.15 g/l is the lowest concentration of lead at which present Western European octane quality can be maintained without significant cost increase (see Table 5.7).

''Besides boosting octane quality, lead in petrol serves to protect hot engine parts from excessive wear by providing a protective and lubricating film. This is particularly significant in preventing 'valve recession', or erosion of valve seats, leading to loss of compression through leakage of combustion gases. The petrol engine has a long history of this problem. Older motorists will remember the regular valve-grinding that had to be carried out every few thousand miles. This was made necessary by the attrition of soft cast-iron cylinder heads by the steel valve heads. The valves themselves were also made of relatively soft steel which tended to erode and pit at a high temperature.

''The use of leaded petrol has alleviated this problem in two ways. Firstly it has led to a general rise in compression ratios, with the result that exhaust gases, and hence valves, have become cooler at any given speed and load. Secondly it interposes a soft layer of lead compounds between the valve seats, which lubricates them and reduces frictional wear.

''Modern valves, although highly stressed by high speeds, strong valve springs and fierce cams, often last the life of the engine without attention. Many modern engines have aluminium cylinder heads, and in some cases, particularly in high performance engines, both the valve seat inserts and the valves themselves are made from special hard material. These function without any problems on unleaded petrol.

''Many family cars, however, for the sake of cheapness continue to have cast-iron cylinder heads with valve seats cut directly into the cast-iron. The presence of lead in petrol allows a high performance valve operation without wear of the soft valve seat. With certain engines the recession problem will begin to occur if lead content drops below 0.12 g/l, but for most engines 0.05 g/l is adequate to prevent it and

36

for this reason BS 4040 currently specifies that as the minimum lead content for "leaded" petrol. In the absence of lead the valve seat must be hardened by a simple process of local heating (by direct flame, or more commonly, by electric induction) and quenching; this, coupled with a slightly superior valve material, is entirely adequate for preventing wear, and adds a negligible amount to manufacturing costs.

"In contrast to its positive effects on engine performance, lead in petrol indirectly has some adverse effects on the durability of certain components of the car. The combustion products of lead alkyls (mainly lead oxides) tend to accumulate in the combustion chamber and cause fouling of spark plugs; to counteract this, ethylene dihalide 'scavengers' (ethylene dichloride and ethylene dibromide) are included with the lead compounds. These convert the non-volatile combustion products into more volatile chlorides and bromides of lead, which are more readily exhausted from the combustion chamber. Despite the use of scavengers, spark plugs may not last as long on leaded petrol as they do on unleaded petrol; and car owners who fail to change plugs at recommended intervals are liable to waste fuel.

"On combustion, ethylene dihalide scavengers generate hydrochloric and hydro-bromic acids, which have a powerful corrosive effect on iron and steel. Mild steel exhaust systems are particularly vulnerable, and maintenance savings are thus possible on unleaded petrol, although external corrosion may for some cars be a more significant factor. Chlorides and bromides also collect in the lubricating oil, where they may cause corrosion of engine parts."

Lead emissions have been shown to depend primarily on driving mode (Figure 2.19) with variations ranging from less than 5 per cent to almost 2000 per cent of the mass of lead entering the combustion chamber. Resuspension of lead particles within the exhaust system is believed to be responsible for the extremely high values. Research has indicated that there are normally two main size groupings of particles in the exhaust emissions: those between 5 -50 μm and those of less than 1 μm aerodynamic diameter. The former represent resuspended particles while the latter represent primary emissions. The primary emissions are composed of particles with an average diameter of 0.015 μm which rapidly coagulate in ambient air due to their high Brownian diffusivity.

This source of atmospheric lead is diminishing in the UK due to the progressive reduction in the lead content of petrol (Table 2.6). As a result of these reductions, UK lead emissions from motor vehicles (comprising both organic and inorganic species) have shown a decrease from 7,400 tonnes in 1975 to 3,000 tonnes in 1987. These figures are based on lead contents for petrol published by the Institute of Petroleum. It has been assumed that only 70 per cent of this lead in petrol is emitted from vehicle exhausts, the remainder being retained in lubricating oil and exhaust systems.

The widespread availability of unleaded petrol and the legal requirement that after April 1991 all new motor vehicles with petrol engines shall be suitable for use with unleaded will further reduce lead levels.

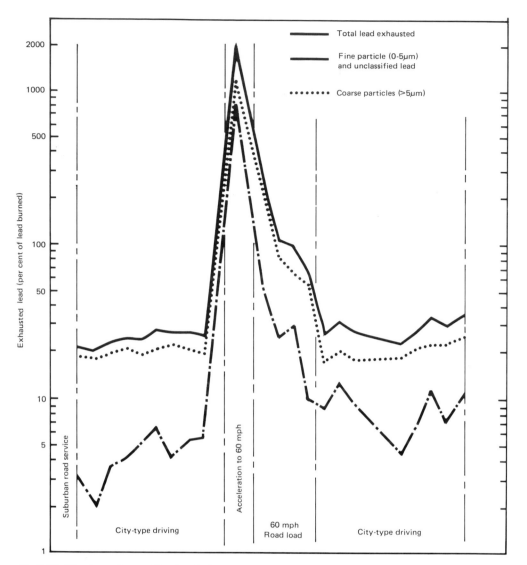

Fig 2.19 The dependence of lead emissions upon driving mode

2.5.9 Polycyclic-aromatic hydrocarbons (PAH)

These are produced at high temperatures during the incomplete combustion and pyrolysis of fossil fuels. With the reduction in the lead content of petrol, the aromatic content has been increased in order to maintain octane levels. The aromatic content of fuel plays a major role in PAH production and displays a linear relationship with particle bonded PAH emissions. The major aromatic compounds present in petroleum are benzene and toluene, ortho-, meta- and para-xylenes and ethylbenzene (Clark *et al.*, 1984). Benzene contributes little to PAH formation whereas C_9 and C_{10} aromatics result in large amounts of PAH in the exhaust.

38

TABLE 2.6

Consumption of petrol and estimated emissions of lead from petrol-engined road vehicles, United Kingdom

| | Consumption of petrol | | Estimated emissions of lead from petrol-engined road vehicles | |
	Million tonnes	*Index 1975 = 100*	*Thousand tonnes*	*Index 1975 = 100*
1975	16.12	100	7.4	100
1976	16.88	105	7.6	103
1977	17.34	108	7.4	100
1978	18.35	114	7.3	99
1979	18.68	116	7.3	99
1980	19.15	119	7.5	101
1981	18.72	116	6.7	91
1982	19.25	119	6.8	92
1983	19.57	121	6.9	93
1984	20.22	125	7.2	97
1985	20.40	127	6.5	88
1986	21.47	133	2.9	39
1987	22.18	138	3.0	40

Source: Department of Energy; Warren Spring Laboratory, Department of Trade and Industry

Exhaust emissions of PAH further depend on air-fuel ratio, type of lubricant and fuel, driving mode, age of vehicle, engine speed, load and torque. Particulate associated PAH emissions vary in a similar manner to the parent particulates with air-fuel ratios, giving high emission rates at very rich and very lean mixtures (Pedersen *et al.*, 1980). Engine lubricants provide convenient intermediates for PAH formation and thus the rate of oil usage affects PAH emissions. High mileage motor vehicles exhibit PAH emissions which increase with speed whereas for low mileage vehicles PAH emissions are relatively constant. Oil consumption is blamed for this phenomenon.

On a mass basis the average emission rates (μg/hr) of total PAH from a light duty petrol engine are about 2-3 times higher than those of a heavy-duty diesel engine. However, the emissions of nitro derivatives of PAH, polycyclic quinones (PQus) and aza hetero-cyclic hydrocarbons (AHHs) are consistently higher from diesel engines. It has been reported that the mutagenicity of diesel exhaust particulates may be much higher than that displayed by gasoline exhaust particulates. Average emission rates, from motor vehicles, for a number of PAH are shown in Table 2.7.

TABLE 2.7

Average Emission Rates of PAH (g/hr at an average speed of 80 km/h)

PETROL ENGINE

	Pyrene	Chrysene	B(a)A	Perylene	B(a)P	B(ghi)P
D	2.8×10^3	1.2×10^2	1.7×10^2	2.9×10^1	1.7×10^2	2.7×10^2
A	8.1×10^3	7.9×10^2	3.8×10^2	6.4×10^1	2.3×10^2	2.9×10^2

DIESEL ENGINE

	Pyrene	Chrysene	B(a)A	Perylene	B(a)P	B(ghi)P
D	1.3×10^3	1.0×10^2	1.6×10^2	1.8×10^1	1.1×10^2	6.5×10^2
A	4.2×10^3	5.4×10^2	3.6×10^2	3.4×10^1	1.0×10^2	1.3×10^2

KEY
B(a)A   = Benzo(a)anthracene
B(a)P   = Benzo(a)pyrene
B(ghi)P = Benzo(ghi)perylene
D   = Tunnel (descending, 1.0% slope, low load)(test condition)
A   = Tunnel (ascending, 0.4% slope, high load)(test condition)

2.6   Chapter 2 References

BENNETT, M, (1987) Mobile measurements of SO_2 in heavy traffic in London, Winter 1983-84. Sci. Tot. Environ. *59* 125-131.

BEVAN, M G and A J HICKMAN, (1974) A mobile laboratory for monitoring air pollution from road vehicles. TRRL Report SR 89, Transport and Road Research Laboratory, Crowthorne.

CLARK, A T, McINTYRE R, PERRY R and J N LESTER, (1984) Monitoring and assessment of ambient atmospheric concentrations of aromatic and halogenated hydro-carbons at urban, rural and motorway locations. Environ. Poll. (B) *7* (2) 141-158.

DEPARTMENT OF THE ENVIRONMENT, (1988) Digest of environmental protection and water statistics, HMSO, London.

FELLOWSHIP OF ENGINEERING, (1987) Manual of acidic emissions abatement techniques, vol 4 - mobile sources. London.

FERRARI L M, JOHNSON, D C and W WATKINS, (1977) Recent techniques for the measurement of sulphur dioxide in the atmosphere. Air pollution analysis. Melbourne Symposium, CASANZ.

HARRISON, R M, and D P H LAXEN, (1984) Lead pollution causes and control. Chapman and Hall.

LATHAM, S and A J HICKMAN, (1990) Exhaust emissions from heavy duty diesel vehicles. Proceedings of Third International Highway Pollution Symposium, Munich, FRG, 1989.

KLEIN, M and F GOURDON, (1982) New method for measuring carbon monoxide in air correlation gas filtration and IR. Pollut. Atmos. *95* 193-199.

PEDERSEN, P S, INGWERSEN J, NEILSON T and E LARSEN, (1980) Effects of fuel, lubricant and engine operating parameters on the emissions of polycyclic aromatic hydrocarbons. Environ. Sci. Technol. *14* (1) 71-79.

PEGG, R E and A W RAMSDEN, (1966) Towards clear diesel engine exhausts, Proc Int. Clean Air Congress 1966, pt 1, 154-6.

PERRY, R and R M HUTCHINSON, (1986) Handbook of air pollution analysis, 2nd Ed. Chapman and Hall.

MIDDLESEX POLYTECHNIC, (1988) Urban Pollution, Research Report No 10.

ROGERS, F S M, (1984) A revised calculation of gaseous emissions from UK motor vehicles, Warren Spring, LR 508 (AP) M.

ROYAL COMMISSION ON ENVIRONMENTAL POLLUTION, (1983) Ninth Report, Lead in the Environment. HMSO, London.

SHERWOOD, P J and P H BOWERS, (1970) Air pollution from road traffic, a review of the present position. TRRL Report LR 352, Transport and Road Research Laboratory, Crowthorne.

WILLIAMS, M L, (1986) The impact of motor vehicles on air pollutant emissions and air quality in the UK - an overview. Second International Symposium on Highway Pollution. Sci. Tot. Environ. *59* 47-62.

3 Emission legislation

3.1 General

It has already been necessary in Chapter 2 to refer to the various drive cycles that are currently laid down by national governments or by international agreement and that consequently have to be understood and used by all vehicle manufacturers and exporters. It is desirable now to give other aspects of legislation, which fall into different groups. The first concerns the actual emissions from vehicle exhausts; the second concerns recommendations regarding air quality; and thirdly it is reasonable to separate out from the first of these those regulations that concern fuel quality, including lead content.

It is also desirable to consider these matters on an international, or at least on a continental, basis, since air pollution is no respecter of frontiers. Unfortunately, so far scientific and rational decision making has tended to be outweighed by political, social and economic differences between countries, with the result that there is no consensus of opinion or agreement on legislation. This is particularly unfortunate with a product such as road vehicles which increasingly travel across national boundaries.

Some large areas of the world do not call for in-depth consideration here. Poorer countries, sometimes called ''developing'' countries, sometimes the ''third world'', have priorities forced upon them that are different from those of wealthier countries. Their first needs are to feed, clothe and shelter their people and to maintain their health as best they can. Problems of pollution understandably play a minor part, and in any case most of them do not have significant vehicle manufacturing capacity. They will thus rely on whatever standards are achieved by the countries from which they import their vehicles. Where, as for example in India, they are working towards legislation, it appears unavoidable that it will lean strongly towards that of the existing quantity vehicle manufacturers. The same arguments apply although to a far lesser extent in Eastern Europe and the countries of the USSR, although these are much closer to the detailed legislation known in the West, and as they proceed it seems likely that they also will tend to adopt Western standards and procedures. The principal regions of the world requiring consideration are the USA, Europe, and Japan.

Legislative requirements fall into two further categories; type approval standards and standards intended to ensure satisfactory in-service performance. Type approval standards require that new model engines or vehicles be tested and that their emission rates do not exceed limit values before their sale is permitted. In-service standards are more diverse and include an obligation to demonstrate the durability of components (for example, catalysts in the USA must endure 50,000 miles of service), periodic testing and maintenance of vehicles for exhaust emission rates, and conformity of production testing. In Sweden, for example, a selection of newly sold vehicles or vehicles offered for sale are tested, and if their emissions do not conform with national requirements the approval certificate may be withdrawn (Egeback, 1986). These in-service standards are so diverse that it will be possible to quote only a sample of them.

3.2   United States of America

3.2.1   Passenger   vehicles

Emission legislation for type approval has developed in the USA for new passenger cars since the mid 1960's (see Table 3.1). USA standards are specified in imperial units, but for consistency are given here metricated.

The legislation is based on the Federal Test Procedure (FTP) drive cycle referred to in Section 2.3.3. This employs a constant volume sampling (CVS) procedure, and includes high engine loads and high vehicle speeds. The cycle begins with a cold start at an ambient temperature near to 70°F.

TABLE 3.1.

Automobile exhaust emission control history, USA. Petrol engined vehicles

Year	Pollutant standard (g/km)(a)		
	CO	HC	NO_x
1968	32	3.7	3.1
1970	21	2.4	3.1
1972	17	1.9	3.1
1973	17	1.9	1.9
1975	9.3	0.9	1.9
1977	9.3	0.9	1.2
1980	4.4	0.25	1.2
1983	2.1	0.25	0.6 (0.9)(b)

(a) Limits to be met after vehicle has been in service for 80,000 km
(b) Value in parenthesis indicates applicable standard for 160,000 km durability.

3.2.2 Light duty commercial vehicles

Legislation for these vehicles was first introduced in the USA in 1975, based on the FTP procedure. The present limits for type approval are given in Table 3.2.

It might be noted that the State of California, prompted by the air conditions in the Los Angeles region, has consistently set lower, tighter standards than the rest of the USA across all vehicle types. It would make presentation too complicated to give them all here.

TABLE 3.2

USA exhaust emission limits, 1988, new light duty vehicles, petrol or diesel, not more than 12 passengers

Law	Emission	Loaded vehicle weight (kg)	dimension	standard LA	HA
CFR40	HC	All	g/km	0.50	0.62
para 86	CO	All	g/km	6.25	8.75
	NO_x	< 1700kg	g/km	0.75	0.75
		> 1700kg		1.06	1.06
	particulates (a)	All	g/km	0.16	0.16
	idle CO (b)	All	vol%	0.50	0.50
	evap. (b)	All	g/test	2.0	2.6
	crankcase emission	All	-	0	0

(a)   only diesel engines
(b)   only petrol engines
LA: low altitude
HA: high altitude 1620m ± 100m

3.2.3 Heavy duty commercial vehicles

Emission legislation for heavy duty vehicles was first introduced in the USA in 1969. Until the beginning of 1985 a steady state 13-mode engine test-bench procedure was utilised, and from the 1985 model year a 20-minute transient emissions test cycle has been adopted. Further changes are proposed for forthcoming years, up to 1994. These values are shown in Table 3.3.

Considerable reductions have been specified in NO_x, and very large further reductions are planned in NO_x and particulates by 1994.

TABLE 3.3

USA exhaust limits, new heavy duty commercial vehicles, from 1969 onwards

| Date | Emission standard value (g/bhp.h) | | | |
	HC	*CO*	*NO$_x$*	*Particulates*
1969	1.3	40.0	16.0(a)	
1985	1.3	25.0	10.7	
1989	1.3	15.5	10.7	0.60
1991-3	1.3	15.5	5.0	0.25(b) 0.10(c)
1994	1.3	15.5	5.0	0.10

(a) HC + NO$_x$
(b) trucks
(c) buses

In addition to the limits set on particulates, visible smoke opacity is measured continuously during a sequence of engine operations on a dynamometer. The test procedure includes two full-load accelerations and a full-load lugdown. The procedure is repeated to give three consecutive valid cycles. During the test, three opacity values are determined:

1. Acceleration. The average of the 15 highest half-second readings during accelerations from each cycle.

2. Lugdown (remove throttle and allow to drop to idle). The average of the 5 highest half-second readings during the lugdown in each cycle.

3. Peak. The average of the three highest half-second readings from each cycle. Current opacity limits are: Acceleration 20 per cent; Lugdown 15 per cent and Peak 50 per cent.

3.2.4   Motorcycles

The motorcycle test procedure uses a drive cycle comparable to that of passenger vehicles in that it is designed to simulate a typical urban trip, and involves both cold and hot engine start-up. The current legislative limits are: HC 5 g/km, and CO 12 g/km.

3.3   Japan

The first emission legislation for vehicles, as measured over a drive cycle, was established in 1973. The tests first employed a 4-mode test cycle, but lately have used two different cycles, the first a 10-mode hot start cycle and the second an 11-mode cold start cycle (for petrol engines), as shown previously in Figure 2.6. Diesel engines are primarily emission tested on a steady-state test bench dynamometer 6-mode cycle.

3.3.1   Petrol engines

Table 3.4 shows how pollutant limits have changed between 1966 and 1978. The 1978 limits are still current. Some comparisons are difficult because of the changes in test procedures, but on the other hand it is obvious that some emissions have been very much reduced, for example, NO_x.

TABLE 3.4

Japan. New automobile exhaust emission control history, petrol engines

Year	Pollutant standard(a)			Unit	Test cycle
	CO	*HC*	NO_x		
1966	3	-	-	%	4 mode
1969	2.5	-	-	%	4 mode
1973	26.0	3.8	3.0	g/km	10 mode
1975	2.7(b)	0.39	1.6	g/km	11 mode
	85.0	9.5	11.0	g/test	11 mode
1976	2.7	0.39	1.2	g/km	10 mode
	85.0	9.5	9.0	g/test	11 mode
1978	2.7	0.39	0.48	g/km	10 mode
	85.0	9.5	6.0	g/test	11 mode

(a) Applicable to all new model vehicles that are greater than 1,000 kg equivalent inertia weight.
(b) The figures show the maximum permissible limits of the standards applicable at 30,000 km durability and apply to new model vehicles only. Although the limits have not changed since 1978, comparison with Table 3.1 for the USA shows that the controls are still fairly severe. Table 3.5 shows the present new vehicle legislation in more detail.

3.3.2   Diesel engines

Table 3.7 shows present legislative levels, in addition to which there exists a smoke test based on a three-mode free acceleration cycle, and measured by timing a filter paper to a 50 per cent opacity. The values shown in the Table are also applied to imported vehicles, using the 10-mode system.

TABLE 3.5.

Japan. New exhaust limits, petrol engines

law: TRIAS 23	Motor vehicles with gasoline engines						
			max. 10 passengers (no wt limitation)		gross vehicle weight >1.7t		
			standards				
test procedure	emissions	dimension	max (1)	mean (2)		max (1)	mean (2)
11 mode	HC CO NOx	g/test	9.50 85.0 6.0	7.0 60.0 4.4		17.0 130 9.50	13.0 100 7.50
10- mode	HC CO NOx	g/km	0.39 2.70 0.48	0.25 2.10 0.25		2.70 17.0 1.26	2.10 13.0 0.90
Idle	HC CO	ppm vol %	max 1200 max 4.5				
trap SHED	evap	g/test	2.0				
	crank-case emissions	-	0				

1) Type approval limit if imported sales figures <2000 and generally as individual limit in series production

2) Type approval limit for domestic manufacturers and as production average (for production control 1% of production has to be tested) if import sales figures ≥2000 vehicles/model year. Japan also has a quite strict regime for the inspection of in-service vehicles (Nakashima, 1986), shown in Table 3.6.

3.4 Europe

The development of legislation in Europe has been, and remains, very complicated. The first comprehensive set of rules was drawn up in 1968 by the United Nations Economic Commission for Europe (ECE) as ECE 15. This has subsequently been subjected to four amendments, to date, hence the headings ECE 15-01 to ECE 15-04. These ECE rules have been in broad terms adopted by the countries of the European Community (EC), and the

TABLE 3.6

In-service exhaust emission test requirements in Japan

Inspection intervals	Category of motor vehicles	Example
1 year	1. Passenger-carrier motor vehicles	Taxis, buses
	2. Motor vehicles for carriage of goods	Trucks, tank lorries
	3. Motor vehicles for private use which are prescribed by Ministry Ordinances	
	a. Motor vehicles for private use whose riding capacity is 11 persons or more	Buses for private use
	b. Motor vehicles for private use which are used exclusively for carriage of children	School buses
	c. Passenger motor vehicles for private use which have been used for more than 10 years (11 years, in the case of motor vehicles which were given a term of three years at their initial inspection)	
2 years	1. Passenger motor vehicles for private use which are more than 10 years old	
	2. Two-wheeled motor vehicles, Large-sized special motor vehicles	
3 years	Passenger motor vehicles for private use less than 10 years old	

TABLE 3.7.

Japan. New exhaust limits, diesel engines

law: TRIAS 24-2	motor vehicles with diesel engines (no weight limitation)		

test procedure	emissions	dim	Standards	
			max 1)	mean 2)
6 - mode		ppm		
	HC_{H-FID}		670	510
	CO		980	790
	NOx		390	290
	NOx (Direct Injection)		610	470

law: TRIAS 24-3	motor vehicles with diesel engines (no weight limitation) with a riding capacity of max 10 passengers		

10 - mode		g/km		
	HC_{H-FID}		0.62	0.40
	CO		2.70	2.10
	NO_x >1265kg vehicle weight		1.26	0.90
	NO_x ≤1265kg vehicle weight		0.98	0.70

48

EC now make independent regulations. Other European countries have generally chosen to adopt either ECE or USA standards. The following discussion concentrates on developments in the EC.

3.4.1   Gaseous pollutants.

Limits for emissions from light duty vehicles were first set in 1970 (Directive 70/220/ EEC), based on the United Nations Regulation ECE 15, (United Nations Economic Commission for Europe, 1968). This specified maximum emission rates for carbon monoxide and hydrocarbons, depending on the weight of the vehicle. Tests were conducted by driving the vehicle on a chassis dynamometer over a slow speed cycle to represent urban driving conditions. Exhaust was sampled using the 'big bag' method, by which all the exhaust gases emitted during the test are collected, and both carbon monoxide and hydrocarbons (as hexane) were measured using infra-red analysers.

A number of amendments continue to be made to the original Directive. The sequence of changes in limits is given in Table 3.8. In 1974, the limit values for carbon monoxide and hydrocarbons were reduced (Directive 74/290/EEC) and in 1977 a standard for oxides of nitrogen emissions was added (Directive 77/102/EEC). Further reductions to

TABLE 3.8

New vehicle exhaust emission control history, EEC   Light-duty vehicles

Year	Directive	Pollutant standard (g/test) ECE Regulation 15 test				
		CO	HC	NOx	HC+NOx	Part
1970[a]	70/220/EEC	100-220	8.0-12.8	-	-	-
1974[a]	74/290/EEC	80-176	6.8-10.9	-	-	-
1977[a]	77/102/EEC	80-176	6.8-10.9	10-16	-	-
1978[a]	78/665/EEC	65-143	6.0- 9.6	8.5-13.6	-	
1983[a]	83/351/EEC	70-132	-	-	23.8-35.0	-
1988[b]	88/76/EEC 88/436/EEC	25-45	-	3.5-6.0	6.5-15	1.1
1989[c]	89/458/EEC	19	-	-	5	-
1990[d]	proposal	2.72[e]	-	-	0.97[c]	0.19[e]

Notes:
a   Standards based on vehicle weight; urban driving cycle
b   Standards based on engine capacity; urban driving cycle
c   For cars with engines <1.41cc only; urban driving cycle
d   For all classes of car; combined urban and extra-urban driving   cycle
e   Standards expressed in g/km

49

the limit values for all three components took place in 1978 (Directive 78/665/EEC). More comprehensive changes took place in 1983 (Directive 83/351/EEC). In addition to a further cut to limit values, the sampling (Section 2.3.3), method was changed from the 'big bag' method to constant volume sampling, by which a known proportion of the exhaust gases is collected, the method for hydrocarbon measurement was changed to flame ionization detection and, for the first time, the Directive applied to diesel as well as petrol engined vehicles.

Following the 1983 Directive, there was a long debate between those who wished to proceed as rapidly as possible to lower pollution levels on environmental grounds and those who argued that economic and industrial considerations should dictate a slower rate of progress. The debate resulted in a number of further amendments to the regulations. In 1985, the "Luxembourg" agreement was reached representing a compromise position. New, lower limits were set, related to the engine capacity rather than the weight of the vehicle (Directive 88/76/EEC). Emission limits were lowest for large cars (>2.0 litre engine displacement) and implied the use of three-way catalysts for compliance; for medium cars (1.4 - 2.0 litre) they were higher and it was thought that a number of technical solutions were possible. Small car (<1.4 litre) limits were highest, with only limited technical changes needed to meet them. In addition, in Directive 88/436/EEC, the first European limits on particulate emissions from diesel powered passenger cars were set. The limit values set by these Directives were higher than levels achievable by the best emission control systems. In the case of gaseous emissions this was because it was felt that the cost penalty to equip vehicles with fully controlled three-way catalysts was excessive, particularly for small cars. The stringency of the particulate standard for diesels was limited by technical difficulties in measuring them accurately and reproducibly.

In view of the continued pressure for environmental improvements, including better control of vehicle emissions, the Commission recognised that these provisions were temporary and indicated its intention to introduce lower limits for both gaseous emissions from small cars and diesel particulates. In parallel, consideration was given to a variety of other additions and amendments to the legislation:

1. The driving cycle for emissions tests was thought no longer to represent driving conditions in Europe adequately. It should be supplemented to include a wider range of vehicle operations, in particular, high speed driving should be included since emission rates at high speeds may be much higher than at low speeds (Pearce, 1987; Joumard, 1987).

2. When emissions are controlled by the use of complex anti-pollution systems, the durability of those systems is important for maintaining low emission rates in service. A durability requirement should be included in the directive.

3. As exhaust hydrocarbon emissions are reduced by the effect of more stringent regulations, evaporative hydrocarbon losses become a major source. Limits should be set for the permissible evaporative hydrocarbon emissions.

4. The appropriateness and legality of fiscal incentives to promote the purchase of

50

low-emission vehicles before the introduction of the new standards should be clarified.

The first formalisation of these latest changes was in 1989 when lower gaseous emission limits for small cars were set (Directive 89/458/EEC). The intention to apply these limits to all sizes of car and the acceptability of "nondiscriminatory", relatively small fiscal incentives were announced at the same time. Subsequently, the Commission has proposed an amending Directive, for application in 1992, that consolidates all of the emission requirements for all categories of passenger cars and addresses the outstanding matters discussed above. In its explanatory memorandum accompanying this proposal, the commission states that "it will be necessary to give the proposed European standards a validity of at least 5 years in order to assure the stability of the legal framework which industry needs to carry out the necessary technical and economic efforts in satisfactory conditions". Because it is therefore likely that standards will remain stable for some time and because of the relatively comprehensive changes that this proposal will introduce, its provisions are given in some detail below.

The proposal gives common emission standards for all cars, irrespective of their engine size or weight. They are based on a test in which the vehicle is driven over a driving cycle that combines the existing urban cycle (Figure 2.7) with an extra-urban cycle that includes speeds up to 120km/h (Figure 2.8) (the development of this cycle is discussed in Pearce and Davies (1990)). In accordance with the intention announced in Directive 89/458/EEC, the limit values to be applied to the combined cycle have been set at a level equivalent to those already established for small cars: ie the introduction of the new cycle should have no effect on the severity of the standards. This was achieved through an extensive comparison of emission rates over the old and new cycles that was carried out at the Commission's request and involved many European motor manufacturers and research organisations, including TRRL. Improvements to the procedure for diesel particulate sampling are specified and, in consequence, lower limits are possible.

Directive 88/76/EEC allowed manufacturers the alternative of certification according to the US "FTP 75" regulations. It is proposed that this option be discontinued after a transitional period of two to three years.

Three alternative durability standards are proposed:

1. The present US durability test which requires the demonstration that control systems' operate satisfactorily after an accumulation of 80,000km. This option is included to allow manufacturers a common standard for certification of models for export to the US.

2. A European durability test requiring only 30,000km accumulation but under more severe conditions than the US test. This is intended for vehicles marketed mainly in the EEC.

3. A set of deterioration factors applicable by manufacturers that do not wish to carry out any durability test. The results obtained during the type approval test must comply with the limit values when multiplied by the deterioration factors.

The existing US procedure for evaporative emissions testing is proposed (the Sealed House Evaporation or SHED test). Evaporative hydrocarbon losses are measured while the vehicle is subjected to a prescribed series of procedures within a sealed chamber. Fuel tank breathing emissions are determined while the fuel in the tank is heated and hot soak emissions are measured after the car has been driven over the combined urban and extra-urban cycle. A formula is given by which the results of the two tests are combined and a limit value of 2g/test is proposed.

Finally, the Commission intends to prepare, at a later date, a proposal on emissions from light commercial vehicles (<3.5 tonnes). These have previously been included in the classes of vehicles covered by the ''light-duty'' limits applicable to passenger cars. In Directive 83/351/EEC, an allowance of 25% above the car standards was made in respect of these vehicles. As a transitional provision before the directive dealing specifically with them is implemented, Directive 88/76/EEC removed the allowance and they became subject to the base standards of Directive 83/351/EEC. The reason for this exception is that light commercial vehicles are thought to differ sufficiently from passenger cars to be treated independently. They have generally much lower power:weight ratios, cannot attain such high speeds and are increasingly fitted with diesel rather than petrol engines.

CO, HC and NO_x standards are also applied to heavy duty diesel engines, with a 13-mode steady state test as specified in Table 3.9.

TABLE 3.9

Test procedure for CO, HC and NO_x (heavy diesels)

Mode	Speed	Load %	Weighting Factor
1	Idle	-	0.08
2	Intermediate	10	0.08
3	Intermediate	25	0.08
4	Intermediate	50	0.08
5	Intermediate	75	0.08
6	Intermediate	100	0.25
7	Idle	-	0.08
8	Rated	100	0.10
9	Rated	75	0.02
10	Rated	50	0.02
11	Rated	25	0.02
12	Rated	10	0.02
13	Idle	-	0.08

Note: Intermediate speed is the speed corresponding with the maximum torque value if that is between 60 and 75% of maximum rated speed. If not then the intermediate speed is 60% of the rated speed.

Weighted average emission rates for the test are calculated and the limit values given in Table 3.10 are applied. The type approval limits apply during certification testing. One or more engines taken from series production may be tested for compliance with the conformity of production limits.

TABLE 3.10.

Limit values for heavy diesels, Europe

| | Standard (g/kW.h) | | |
	CO	HC	NOx
Type approval[a]	11.2	2.4	14.4
Conformity of production[a]	12.3	2.6	15.8
Type approval[b]	14.0	3.5	18.0
Conformity of production[b]	14.0	3.5	18.0

Notes

a   European Community Directive 88/77/EEC. May be applied by Member States (including UK) from 1 October 1990. These standards are anticipated, on a voluntary basis, in FRG and the Netherlands.

b   Economic Commission for Europe Regulation 49. Applied currently in Czechoslovakia, France, Finland, Italy (voluntary) and Spain. Austrian limits are lower by 20%. Swiss limits are lower by 40% for CO and HC and 20% for NOx.

3.4.2   Smoke and particulate emissions

A dual test procedure is applied for smoke opacity. Firstly, smoke readings are measured at six engine speeds evenly spaced between the speed of maximum torque and the higher of 45% of that speed or 1000 rev/min. The limit values are specified in light absorption coefficient units as a function of the nominal exhaust gas flowrate (Figure 3.1). Secondly, the peak smoke opacity during free acceleration is measured. (The free acceleration test consists of a series of rapid accelerations from idle to governor run-out speed with no externally applied load. Sufficient repeats are carried out to provide a series of six consecutive readings within a prescribed opacity tolerance and that do not form an ascending or descending series). For turbo charged engines, the average of four stabilized readings must not exceed the limit for the nominal flow corresponding with the highest absorption coefficient measured during the steady state part of the test by more than 0.5 m^{-1}.

The test is specified in the European Community Directive 72/306/EEC and the Economic Commission for Europe Regulation 24. It is applied in Belgium, Finland,

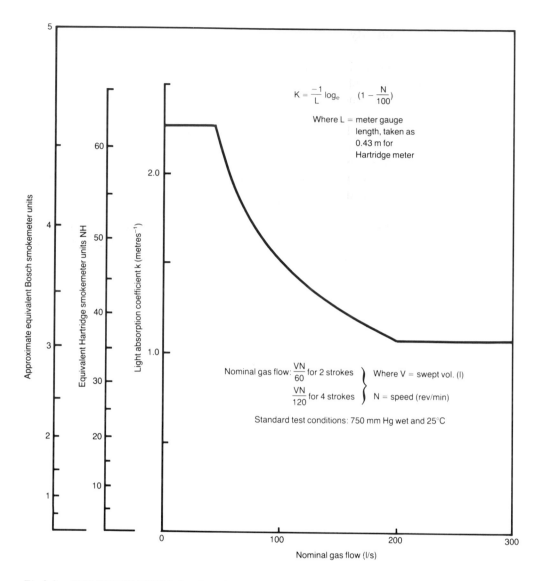

Fig 3.1   ECE 24/EEC 72/306 diesel engine exhaust smoke limits

France, Italy, Spain, Switzerland and the United Kingdom. Sweden applies separate smoke standards for buses (2.5 Bosch) and other diesel engined vehicles (3.5 Bosch).

Particulate mass emissions will be applied as an additional limit to the gaseous emission test described above. Norway proposes a limit of 0.4 g/kW.h; Sweden a limit set to represent best current technology and Switzerland 0.7 g/kW.h from 1 October 1991. As with future gaseous emission limits, the European Commission is considering a particulate mass standard for the second stage of the implementation of Directive 88/77/EEC.

3.5 Air quality

Although emission legislation as described in earlier sections of this Chapter is the obvious method of reducing emissions and thereby improving air quality, the ultimate goal is still the improvement of the quality of the air itself and it would be convenient if simple relationships existed between emission levels and air quality that could lead to definitions of what air quality should be. This however is not the case. The problems of defining air quality standards involve health effects, subjective effects to do with nuisance, and ecological effects, all of which will be discussed in the next Chapter. Even in the most direct of these - health - the relationship between human disease and exposure to pollution is neither simple nor fully understood.

Death and disease represent only the extreme end of a whole spectrum of responses, and the issue is further complicated by the fact that some groups within the population may be especially sensitive to environmental factors, particularly the very young, the very old, those already afflicted with illness, and those exposed to other toxic materials or stresses.

3.5.1 Air pollution goals

When using air quality criteria and guides to evaluate risks and set standards, one should ideally have available a complete set of dose-response curves for the different pollutants, for different effects, and for the different types of population involved. A World Health Organisation Committee stated in 1972 (WHO, 1972) that this requirement had not yet been satisfied for any single substance and was even further from being met for the combinations of substances found in the ambient air. There seems to be no reason why a similar report should come to a different conclusion now.

Nevertheless, the Committee did agree that certain levels of air pollutants, in their best judgement, were associated with adverse effects on health. They pointed out the political and financial problems involved in the preparation of standards, saying that the acceptance of a standard based upon a statistical concept means that it might not confer protection on every individual.

They also drew a distinction between short-term goals, which they said will evolve differently in various countries depending on exposure conditions, on the socio-economic situation and other factors, and long-term goals which might offer the hope that limits on pollution could be set at levels which would produce no ill effects at all. Their recommended relevant, somewhat speculative, long-term goals were as follows in Table 3.11.

It has been pointed out elsewhere (Williams, 1987) that vehicle emissions affect air quality differently in different regions; (a) the kerbside or immediate neighbourhood (within 1-3m) of the roadside; (b) the urban background; and (c) rural or remote areas. In region (a) vehicles in general provide the greater part of local primary pollutant concentrations. For CO, vehicles contribute 85 per cent of total UK emissions so that in

55

TABLE 3.11.

Recommended long-term air pollution goals, W.H.O, 1972

Pollutant and measurement method	Period	Limiting level (g/m^3)
Sulphur oxides - BS Procedure	Annual mean	60
	98 per cent of observations below	200
Suspended particulates - BS Procedure(a)	Annual mean	40
	98 per cent of observations below	120
Carbon monoxide - nondispersive infrared	8-hour average	10
	1-hour maximum	40
Photochemical-oxidant as measured by neutral buffered K1 method expressed as ozone	8-hour average	60
	1-hour maximum	120

(a) methods are not necessarily those recommended, but are those on which these units are based.

busy streets the vehicular contribution is likely to be as much as 95 per cent. Vehicles contribute 40 per cent nationally of NO_x in the UK with a similar amount coming from power stations which emit from tall stacks, normally some distance from busy streets. It has been estimated (EEC Group ERGA, 1982) that, because of this, vehicles contribute at least 85 per cent of the NO_x measured at, as an example, a kerbside site at Cromwell Road in West London. Reductions in vehicle emissions as a result of future legislation will therefore mean that to a good approximation concentrations of CO and NO_x will reduce proportionally, provided that traffic speeds and driving patterns do not alter.

For type (b) areas, traffic contributions to CO concentrations will be greater than the 85 per cent national average, but less than 95 per cent. Here, as for the kerbside, it is probable that reductions in vehicle emissions will result in approximately proportional reductions in ambient concentrations, provided that no significant changes take place in traffic flow patterns. In these areas, vehicles contribute between 60 and 85 per cent of the concentration of NO_x depending upon local circumstances.

3.5.2 USA Standards

The National Ambient Air Quality Standards (NAAQS) were established in the USA in 1970, as were the control strategies used to attain and/or maintain quality at or better than the promulgated values, ie at or better than levels that are considered safe for the public.

There are two types of NAAQS, primary and secondary. A primary NAAQS has a value sufficient to maintain the public health, allowing an adequate margin of safety, whilst a secondary NAAQS is a more severe standard intended "to protect the public welfare from any known or anticipated effects associated with presence of such air pollutant in the ambient air".

"Public welfare" has a very broad definition, including effects on many things, including weather, visibility, climate, vegetation, water, and other items. To establish a NAAQS an Administrator of the Environmental Protection Agency needs to judge that the pollutant under question has an adverse effect, and he then notifies the public, through a Federal Register, of his intent to publish a NAAQS for that pollutant. Within 12 months he must then issue an "air quality criteria document" setting out the nature and extent of the problem, and the scientific basis for determining the NAAQS values.

At the same time, a document on control techniques must be published, together with primary and secondary values. It is then the duty of each State to decide a procedure for achieving these standards, to the satisfaction of the Administrator, and a tight time-table is laid down for this to be done.

This means the air in all parts of the USA was required to meet the national primary standards set out in Table 3.12 by 1977 at the latest, and secondary standards were to be achieved within a "reasonable time".

3.5.3   EEC Standards

At Community level, there exist at the moment air quality standards for SO_2, suspended particulate matter (SPM), NO_2, and atmospheric lead. The relevant EEC Directives are 80/779/EEC for SO_2 and SPM; 85/203/EEC for NO_2; and 82/884/EEC for lead. No air quality standard for CO has yet been agreed, and attempts to do so have always failed because of arguments such as the one that smokers inhale CO from the tobacco, and so do others breathing in the smoke that they produce. Neither does the EEC yet have a standard for hydrocarbons, or photochemical oxidants, of which ozone O_3 is the most commonly measured substance.

There is a clear distinction made, as elsewhere, between what are called "limit values", ie short-term values, and "guide values", ie tighter values that it is hoped might be reached in the future. The following Tables (3.13 to 3.18) give the values contained in the above Directives.

SO_2 and suspended particulates are considered together, the values for one being linked with the values for the other. It has also been considered necessary to allow for two different methods of measurement, one being a "black smoke" system operated by some countries in accordance with an OECD procedure, and the other a gravimetric method detailed in 80/779/EEC. The values in Tables 3.14 to 3.17 are considered to correspond. Table 3.14 illustrates the "linking" referred to, where, for example, the limit value of 80 for SO_2 relates only to a particulate value of over 40.

TABLE 3.12.

National primary and secondary ambient air quality standards - USA

Pollutant	Concentration Limit		Averaging Time
	Micrograms per Cubic Meter	*Parts per Million*	
Carbon monoxide	10,000	9	8 hours[a]
	40,000	35	1 hour[a]
Photochemical oxidants	160[c]	0.08	1 hour[a]
Hydrocarbons (methane free)	160	0.24	3 hours[a]
Nitrogen oxides	100	0.05	1 year
Sulphur oxides	80	0.03	1 year
	365	0.14	24 hours[a]
	(60)	(0.02)	(1 year)
	(260)	(0.1)	(24 hours)[a]
	(1,300)	(0.5)	(3 hours)[a]
Particulate matter	75	-	1 year[b]
	260	-	24 hours[a]
	(60)	-	(1 year)[b]
	(150)	-	(24 hours)[a]

Note: Secondary standards are shown in parentheses; for some pollutants the secondary standards are the same as the primary standards.
[a] Not to be exceeded more than once a year.
[b] Geometric mean.
[c] Raised in 1979 to 235, not to be exceeded more than once a year.

TABLE 3.13

EEC limits for NO_2; 85/203/EEC

concentration (g/m^3)	Remarks
200	limit value over 1 year (1)
50	guide value (2)
135	guide value (1)

(1) 98th percentile calculated from mean values per hour or per period of less than 1 hour recorded throughout the year.
(2) 50th percentile calculated as (1).

TABLE 3.14

EEC Limit values for sulphur dioxide and suspended particulates (as measured by the black-smoke method)

Reference period	Limit value for sulphur dioxide g/m	Associated value for suspended particles g/m3
Year	80 (median of daily mean values taken throughout the year)	>40 (median of daily mean values taken throughout the year)
	120 (median of daily mean values taken throughout the year)	≤40 (median of daily mean values taken throughout the year)
Winter (1 October to 31 March)	130 (median of daily mean values taken throughout the winter)	>60 (median of daily mean values taken throughout the winter)
	180 (median of daily mean values taken throughout the winter)	≤60 (median of daily mean values taken throughout the winter)
Year (Made up of units of measuring periods of 24 hours)	250(2) (98 percentile of all daily mean values taken throughout the year)	>150 (98 percentile of all daily mean values taken throughout the year)
	350(2) (98 percentile of all daily mean values taken throughout the year)	≤150 (98 percentile of all daily mean values taken throughout the year)

(1)The results of the measurements of black smoke taken by the OECD method have been converted into gravimetric units as described by the OECD.
(2)Member States must take all appropriate steps to ensure that this value is not exceeded for more than three consecutive days. Moreover, Member States must endeavour to prevent and reduce any such instances in which this value has been exceeded.

TABLE 3.15

EEC Limit values for suspended particulates (as measured by the black-smoke method(1)) expressed in g/m^3

Reference period	Limit value for suspended particulates
Year	80 (median of daily mean values taken throughout the year)
Winter (1 October to 31 March)	130 (median of daily mean values taken throughout the winter)
Year (made up of units of measuring periods of 24 hours)	250(2) (98 percentile of all daily mean values taken throughout the year)

(1) The results of the measurements of black smoke taken by the OECD method have been converted into gravimetric units as described by the OECD.
(2) Member States must take all appropriate steps to ensure that this value is not exceeded for more than three consecutive days. Moreover, Member States must endeavour to prevent and to reduce any such instances in which this value has been exceeded.

TABLE 3.16

EEC guide values for sulphur dioxide and suspended particulates (as measured by the black-smoke method(1))

Reference period	Guide value for sulphur dioxide or suspended particles ($\mu g/m^3$)
Year	40 to 60 (arithmetic mean of daily mean values taken throughout the year)
24 hours	100 to 150 (daily mean value)

(1)The results of the measurements of black smoke taken by the OECD method have been converted into gravimetric units as described by the OECD

TABLE 3.17

Limit values for sulphur dioxide and suspended particulates (as measured by a gravimetric method)

TABLE A
Limit values for sulphur dioxide expressed in g/m^3

Reference period	Guide value for sulphur dioxide
Year	140 (arithmetic mean of 30 minute values taken throughout the year)
Year (made up of units of measuring periods of 30 minutes)	400 (95 percentile of all 30 minute values taken throughout the year)

TABLE B
Limit values for suspended particulates (as measured by the gravimetric method) expressed in g/m^3

Reference period	Guide value for sulphur dioxide
Year	150 (arithmetic mean of daily mean values taken throughout the year)
Year (made up of units of measuring periods of 24 hours)	300 (95 percentile of all daily mean values taken throughout the year)

TABLE 3.18

Limit for lead; 82/884/EEC

Pollutant Value	(g/m^3)	Remarks
Lead	2	Annual mean concentration

3.5.4   Some standards from individual countries

A paper (EEC Group ERGA, 1982) produced for the EEC in 1982 by the Motor Vehicle Working Group of the ad-hoc group "ERGA-Air Pollution" listed many relevant air quality standards. For CO, 16 countries are listed as having limit values, including some EEC countries. West Germany has the strictest standards of the EEC countries, quoting $30mg/m^3$ over 30 minutes and 10 mg/m^3 as a yearly mean. It is interesting that East Germany, the USSR and Yugoslavia are quoted as having limit values of only 1 mg/m^3 over 24 hours. Japan is quoted as requiring 23 mg/m^3 over 8 hours, and 11 mg/m^3 over 24 hours.

Three countries - Italy, Israel, and the USA, have limits for hydrocarbons (HC). Italy and Israel both have overall standards, the tighter being that of Israel, for whom the paper quotes 5 mg/m^3 over 30 minutes and 2 mg/m^3 over 24 hours. The quoted USA limit is 160 $\mu g/m^3$ over 3 hours but as a NAAQS for non-methane HC only.

NO_2 and NO standards are widely set, 19 countries being listed. These are very variable, and standards are set over a wide range of conditions. However some rough comparisons are possible. For example, considering a 24 hour period, on the basis of $\mu g/m^3$, the Netherlands set 100 to 150 depending on the way it is calculated; Finland, Norway, Spain, France, Italy, and Canada all 200; Japan 75 to 100; USA 100, USSR 85 and East Germany only 40.

Standards for lead particulates are listed for 12 countries. 24 hour averages range for Eastern Europe and the USSR around 1 $\mu g/m^3$, whilst the EEC value is 2. Other countries use different periods for averaging; 8 hour averages for Spain and 10 for Italy.

Almost every country has limit values for SO_2, again based upon different periods for taking averages. There are also large differences depending upon the nature of the site and its exposure, and the nature of the source. These are so great that there is no point in quoting numbers here, and in any case SO_2 is not primarily a product of motor vehicles.

O_3 is relevant, and 5 countries are listed as having limit value standards. One hour average limits range from 160 $\mu g/m^3$ in Japan to 235 in the USA. Canada differentiates between 160 for the "maximum acceptable" and 300 for the "maximum tolerable".

Particulate matter (SPM) has limit standards in 19 countries. As with SO_2 the variation is very great, and so is the type of exposure and source to which they are related. Some figures that are more or less comparable for 24 hour averages are: France, Norway, USSR, all 150; Italy, Spain 300; Sweden, USA 260; Poland 200; and Japan 100 - all based upon $\mu g/m^3$.

The United Kingdom does not appear separately in this list, but has now adopted the EEC standards. It should be pointed out that, in any of these countries, the existence of a "standard" does not necessarily mean that air quality always meets that standard.

3.6 Fuel quality

3.6.1 Petrol

Clearly the most important development at the moment is the increasing availability and use of low lead and unleaded petrol, the purpose and nature of which is discussed elsewhere. Unleaded petrol has been available for a very long time in the USA, and in Europe EEC Directive 85/210/EEC required member states to make unleaded widely available by October 1988. This can reasonably be claimed to have happened.

The rate at which unleaded petrol will continue to be taken up depends not only on the rate of phasing out of vehicles which are not capable of running on it, but also on the fiscal policies employed in different countries for leaded and unleaded fuels: several countries, including the UK, levy lower rates of tax on unleaded fuel.

In order to maintain the Octane number at 95 in unleaded petrol the relative concentrations of other high octane compounds must be increased. Important among these are aromatic hydrocarbons and EEC Directive 85/210/EEC sets a limit of 5 per cent on the benzene content of unleaded petrol. It is important in the future to safeguard against a possible rise in the total aromatic content of petrol, which could have an effect on the formation of photochemical ozone. Also benzene is carcinogenic, and high aromatic fuel produces high PAH.

In the United Kingdom, standards for fuel quality are laid down by the British Standards Institution, BS4040:1985 covering leaded petrol, and BS7070:1985 covering unleaded. Grade designations are determined by both RON and MON tests for limiting anti-knock conditions (see Section 2.5.8), and sampling and testing procedures are tightly specified. Some relevant general requirements for all grades, as quoted in the Standards, are given in Table 3.19.

3.6.2 Diesel

The properties of diesel fuel have a great effect not only on emissions, but also on the performance of engines as measured by the 'cetane number', which is an engine parameter derived from the ignition delay after injection measured using a standard procedure. This 'number' is not itself a completely satisfactory indicator because of the difficulty of relating it to other engine characteristics. It is beyond the scope of this paper to go into these problems in detail, but it is due to these and similar complications that diesel engine emission legislation has been and remains lagging behind legislation relating to petrol engines.

Reductions in the cetane number, or increases in the total aromatic content, usually produce more smoke, gaseous hydrocarbons and NO_x. Particulate emissions are also increased by increasing the sulphur content of the fuel.

TABLE 3.19

Some BS requirements for all grades of petrol

Property	Leaded (BS4040)		Unleaded (BS7070)	
	Min	Max	Min	Max
Water and suspended matter	-	none visible	-	none visible
Sulphur content percent by weight	-	0.2	-	0.2
Existent gum (solvent washed) mg/100mL	-	5	-	5
Lead content g/L	0.05	0.15	-	0.013
Benzene content percent by volume	-	-	-	5

During the last twenty years the quality of diesel fuel has dropped markedly, particularly in the USA where the cetane number has fallen from about 50 to 43. It is anticipated that this will also happen in Europe as the petroleum industry attempts to extract a higher percentage of this type of fuel from each barrel. There are now available some cetane improving additives which raise the cetane value of a poorer fuel to a higher value, with corresponding beneficial effects on exhaust emissions.

In the United Kingdom standards for diesel fuel are determined by British Standard BS/2869/1988.

3.7 Chapter 3 References

EEC GROUP ERGA, (1982) Air Pollution. Air quality standards relevant to pollution from motor vehicles. Brussels.

EGEBACK, K E, (1986) Experience gained with the adoption of US American exhaust gas emission regulations. Proc. of the Conference ''Das schadstoffarme Automobil'' Verlag TUV Rheinland, Cologne.

JOURMARD, R, (1987) Influence of speed limits on road and motorway on pollutant emissions. The Science of the Total Environment, Vol 59, pp87-96.

NAKASHIMA, T, (1986) How to incorporate motor vehicles exhaust gas purification schemes into the overall strategy devised for maintaining ambient air quality - effects on pollution concentration. Proc. Conference ''Das schadstoffarme Automobil'' Verlag TUV Rheinland, Cologne.

PEARCE, T C, (1987) Vehicle emissions at high speeds. The science of the total environment, Vol 59, pp77-86.

PEARCE, T C and G P DAVIES, (1990) The development of an extra-urban driving cycle for exhaust emission measurements. TRRL Research Report 194, Transport and Road Research Laboratory, Crowthorne.

WHO EXPERT COMMITTEE, (1972) Air Quality Criteria and Guides for Urban Air Pollutants. Technical Report Series No 506, Geneva.

WILLIAMS, M L (1987) Relating vehicle emission regulations to air quality. Proc. Inst. Mech. E. Conference, Vehicle emissions and their impact on European air quality.

4 Environmental effects

This chapter will discuss the effects of exhaust emissions on the environment, using the word "environment" to cover in a broad way the impacts of such air pollution on the quality of life. These will be divided into three main sub-heads of health effects; subjective effects; and ecological effects which, for want of a better term, will be taken to include the "greenhouse" effect and other matters. It should, however, be realised that such a division is to a large extent artificial, since they are all inter-related. For example, a press report of a study of the harmful effects of lead will trigger a subjective reaction against the exhaust odour from a diesel vehicle the next time one is smelt, although there is no actual relationship between the two. In addition, some gases that need to be considered in a study of acidity are also among those responsible for the "greenhouse" effect, and some ecological effects may also have implications for health.

4.1 Health effects

4.1.1 Carbon monoxide

The toxic properties of this gas are due to its ability to react with the haemoglobin in the blood to produce carboxy-haemoglobin (COH_b). Carbon monoxide has a greater affinity for haemoglobin than oxygen and it is preferentially absorbed even when the concentration of carbon monoxide is very low. The degree of absorption depends on the concentration of carbon monoxide in the air, the periods of exposure and the activity of the individual. The levels of carboxy-haemoglobin in the blood for different concentrations of carbon monoxide in the atmosphere are given in Table 4.1. The toxic effects of carbon monoxide as measured by the percentage of carboxy-haemoglobin in the blood are given in Table 4.2.

After a subject ceases to be exposed to non-lethal doses of carbon monoxide, the carboxy-haemoglobin content of the blood gradually declines (by 50 per cent in 3 to 4 hours) as carbon monoxide is breathed out. The concentrations that show serious problems in Table 4.2 are much greater than those likely to be experienced by road users, or others, due to vehicle exhausts. The tightest European air quality standard for CO (see Chapter 3, section 3.5.4) is that of West Germany where there is a limit value of 30 mg/m^3 over 30 minutes. 30 mg/m^3 is about 26 ppm, and this from Table 4.1 would produce less than one per cent COH_b. The highest concentrations of COH_b are found on the road among police, highway and garage workers, and others exposed for long periods to exhaust fumes. During a day's work such people have been found to exhibit COH_b concentrations up to 8 per cent for smokers, but only 4 per cent for non-smokers, both within the "no signs or symptoms" range. Indeed, heavy smokers can exhibit COH_b

TABLE 4.1

Carboxy-haemoglobin content of blood (in terms of percentage of full absorption) for different concentrations of carbon monoxide in the atmosphere

Concentration of carbon monoxide in the atmosphere (ppm)	Equilibrium of COH_b in the blood (per cent)	COH_b in the blood after 30 min exposure (per cent)		COH_b in the blood after 60 min exposure (per cent)	
		Rest	Heavy work	Rest	Heavy work
30	4.8	0.27	0.99	0.54	1.98
50	8.0	0.45	1.65	0.90	3.30
125	20	1.12	4.12	2.24	8.24
250	40	2.25	8.24	4.50	16.48

TABLE 4.2

Signs and symptoms at various concentrations of carboxy-haemoglobin

Per cent COH_b	Signs and symptoms for an average man
0-10	No signs or symptoms
10-20	Tightness across the forehead, possible slight headache, dilation of the cutaneous blood vessel
20-30	Headache and throbbing in the temples
30-40	Severe headache, weakness, dizziness, dimness of vision, nausea, vomiting and collapse.
40-50	Same as above, greater possibility of collapse, syncope and increased pulse and respiratory rates
50 60	Syncope, increased pulse rate, coma, intermittent convulsions, and Cheyne-Stokes respiration
60-70	Coma, intermittent convulsions, depressed heart action and respiratory rate, and possible death
70-80	Weak pulse, slow respirations, respiratory failure and death within a few hours
80-90	Death in less than an hour
90+	Death within a few minutes

concentrations up to 15 per cent from that source alone (WHO, 1979). "Although this seems a clear indication that carbon monoxide is not likely to leave any permanent effects or cause any acute physical discomfort to most people its effects cannot be entirely discounted. Apart from relatively minor physical discomfort in particularly susceptible people quite small amounts of COH_b in the blood have been shown to impair temporarily mental ability (Beard, 1967) and Schulte (Schulte, 1963) claims that perception is reduced on levels of less than 5 per cent. This can affect driving ability. Also, the impaired oxygen transport in the human body can have serious implications for persons with pre-existing heart or lung pathology (WHO, 1979), and for the foetuses carried by pregnant women.

4.1.2 Oxides of nitrogen

Both nitric oxide (NO) and nitrogen dioxide (NO_2) are produced by internal combustion engines, the former in much larger quantities than the latter. However NO oxidises to NO_2 and typical ambient atmospheres in city streets contain about half as much NO_2 as NO. Their toxicity is by no means equal, NO_2 being very much more toxic than NO - the MAC (maximum allowable concentration for industrial exposures of 8h) are NO 25ppm, and NO_2 5ppm. Normal levels in city streets are under 1 per cent of these values, and little information is thus available on their effects on humans. Such studies as have been carried out indicate that exposure to NO_2 can be linked with increased susceptibility to respiratory infection, increased airway resistance in asthmatics, and decreased pulmonary function (Walsh, 1988). Short term exposures to NO_2 have resulted in a wide ranging group of respiratory problems in school children, such as coughs and sore throats, although at concentrations typically higher than normal air quality standards. The possibility of effects from continuous exposure to very low levels remains a worry, and there is also the possibility of adverse effects resulting from the absorption of NO_x on the carbon particles produced from exhausts.

4.1.3 Photochemical oxidants

Where there is a high emission of hydrocarbons and NO_x together with long periods of sunshine there frequently occur chemical reactions in the atmosphere producing photochemical oxidants. This first became widely known in Los Angeles, USA during the 1950's, but now is known to occur in many other parts of the world.

The photochemical processes are complex, take place over several hours, and result in the formation of ozone (O_3), nitrogen dioxide (NO_2), peroxyacetyl nitrate (PAN), a variety of other gaseous compounds that are poorly defined, and very fine particulate matter. The O_3, NO_2 and PAN are highly active oxidising chemicals and are responsible for most of the injury and damage produced by this type of air pollution. The fine particulate matter, which consists mainly of nitrates and sulphates, interferes considerably with visibility and is one of the major annoyance factors. Another is the eye irritation caused partly by PAN and partly by other chemicals in the poorly defined group, such as formaldehyde and acrolein, (WHO, 1981).

Ozone is the strongest of the photochemically-formed oxidants that are stable enough to be identified and measured. It is also known to be highly toxic and the evidence, according to the World Health Organisation, for "attributing many adverse effects solely to ozone is very compelling". Studies have shown that many people, even healthy young children, suffer adverse effects from exposure to ozone at quite low levels, including eye irritation, coughs, chest discomfort, headaches, respiratory illness, increased asthma attacks, and reduced pulmonary function. The WHO have recently said:

> "Existing data on the health effects of ozone, considered in conjunction with its high natural background level, lead to the recommendation of a 1-hour guideline in the range of 150-200 $\mu g/m^3$ (0.076-0.100 ppm)."

To lessen the potential for adverse acute and chronic effects, and to provide an additional margin of protection, an 8-hour guideline for exposure to ozone of 100 - 200 $\mu g/m^3$ (0.05 - 0.06 ppm) was recommended.

These values are frequently exceeded in many countries, including the United Kingdom. A report (UK Photochemical Oxidants Review Group, 1987) published at the request of the UK Department of the Environment stated:

> "At rural sites during the period September to March, maximum hourly mean ozone concentrations are typically 10 to 30 ppb, but may be over 40 ppb on some days between February to March. At rural sites there is a summer baseline of 20-40 ppb during the April to August period and some days have maximum hourly mean ozone concentrations over 60 ppb.

> "At every site both urban and rural, hourly mean concentrations in excess of 60 ppb have been observed and these are normally during the period April to September. The number of hours with concentrations over 60 ppb is generally between 100 and 200 in each year.

> "The number of hours with hourly mean ozone concentrations exceeding 80, 100 and 120 ppb at rural or urban sites is typically up to 100, 10-50 and up to 10 in each year."

Table 4.3 (From Ashmore, 1984) gives the maximum hourly mean ozone concentrations recorded at various sites in the UK, over a period of 14 years. For comparison, Table 4.4 gives figures covering part of the same period for five sites in the Federal Republic of Germany (Innes and Boswell, 1987). Although the sites in the above two tables are not necessarily completely representative of the whole of the UK or the FRG, it is interesting to try to compare the values given. Table 4.5 shows the range of the highest and the lowest maximum hourly values, for the six years common to both tables. They would appear to be describing very similar conditions.

69

TABLE 4.3

Maximum hourly mean ozone concentration (ppb) recorded at each site 1972-1985

Site no Site name	1972	1973	1974	1975	1976	1977	1978	1979	1980	1981	1982	1983	1984	1985
3 DEVILLA	-	-	-	-	-	-	99	74	-	-	-	-	-	-
4 GLASGOW	-	-	-	-	-	-	-	-	-	-	-	104	82	108
6 EAST KILBRIDE	-	-	-	118	-	-	-	-	-	-	-	-	-	-
10 WRAY	-	-	-	-	-	-	-	-	-	-	-	-	-	88
11 HEYSHAM	-	-	-	-	-	110	120	122	-	-	-	-	-	-
12 STODDAY	-	-	-	-	-	-	-	-	-	-	133	156	120	-
13 HAZELRIGG	-	-	-	-	-	-	-	-	-	99	-	-	-	-
26 BOTTESFORD	-	-	-	-	-	-	144	120	156	79	111	99	107	109
28 SIBTON	-	-	-	-	104	113	127	100	63	207	124	133	124	96
29 STEVENAGE	-	-	-	-	207	135	100	108	84	68	164	168	174	122
30 ST.OSYTH	-	-	-	-	-	-	-	-	-	-	-	-	-	144
32 CHIGWELL	-	-	-	-	-	-	-	128	-	-	119	114	160	-
33 HAINAULT	-	-	-	122	178	-	-	-	-	-	-	-	-	-
35 HARROW	-	-	-	-	-	-	-	180	110	-	-	-	-	-
36 HARWELL	124	141	120	177	258	121	114	-	-	-	152	141	114	102
37 CANVEY ISLE	-	-	-	-	-	179	147	93	77	-	-	-	-	-
38 ISLINGTON	-	-	-	-	117	127	98	-	-	-	-	-	-	-
40 NAT. WEST TR	-	-	-	-	-	-	-	-	-	-	-	106	-	-
41 COUNTY HALL	-	-	-	150	212	87	103	153	116	112	91	99	88	98
42 LONDON Cent.	126	136	163	92	144	99	149	95	76	128	78	77	68	149
43 CROMWELL RD	-	100	45	-	-	-	-	-	-	-	-	-	-	-
45 KEW	-	-	-	-	-	-	-	156	-	-	-	-	-	-
46 CARDIFF	-	-	71	-	-	-	-	-	-	-	-	-	-	-
48 TEDDINGTON	-	-	-	138	211	-	157	-	-	123	137	117	136	-
49 ASCOT	136	-	-	-	-	122	133	137	105	118	123	153	113	82
54 EAST MALLING	-	-	-	-	-	-	-	-	-	-	-	-	111	126
57 CHILWORTH	-	-	-	173	-	-	-	-	-	-	-	-	-	-

Not Operational = -

TABLE 4.4

Ozone concentrations (ppb) at five monitoring stations in the Federal Republic of Germany. From: UBA Monatsberichte, 1986: summarised in Department of the Environment (1987b)

Station	Year	98% percentile Year	98% percentile Summer	Percentage > 75 ppb	Percentage > 100 ppb	Max. hourly means	Annual means
Westerland	1980	58	62	<0.1	0	75	31
(Sylt Island)	1981	61	67	0.2	0	84	32
	1982	49	52	0.0	0	63	29
	1983	-	-	-	-	-	-
	1984	57	64	0.5	0	96	29
	1985	56	61	0.2	0	83	30
Deuselbach	1980	80	92	2.5	0.5	145	31
(Central	1981	65	74	0.9	0	97	29
Germany)	1982	74	81	1.8	0.1	110	28
	1983	64	69	0.5	0	92	27
	1984	65	69	0.4	0	94	27
	1985	65	72	0.7	0	98	26
Waldhof	1979	88	96	4.7	0.9	127	34
(Northern	1980	79	89	2.8	0.4	122	30
German	1981	73	110	2.0	0.0	135	19
Plain)	1982	80	90	2.6	0.3	115	27
	1983	102	113	7.1	2.2	160	42
	1984	57	66	0.4	0	91	25
	1985	78	99	2.4	0.9	143	25
Schauinsland	1980	101	109	14.7	2.0	179	56
(Black Forest)	1981	70	69	1.1	0	90	40
	1982	85	92	5.1	0.5	133	45
	1983	85	94	4.9	0.5	127	45
	1984	88	94	7.8	0.5	120	47
	1985	76	81	2.5	<0.1	101	43
Brotjacklriegel	1980	57	61	0.1	0	81	32
(Bavarian	1981	75	78	2.0	0	97	40
Forest)	1982	82	87	4.6	0.1	104	42
	1983	83	87	5.6	<0.1	112	42
	1984	72	79	1.5	0.1	102	33
	1985	67	72	0.5	0	87	34

TABLE 4.5

Range of maximum hourly ozone concentrations, UK and FRG, ppb.

Year	UK	FRG
1980	63-156	75-179
1981	68-207	84-135
1982	78-207	63-133
1983	77-168	92-160
1984	68-174	91-120
1985	82-149	83-143

4.1.4   Lead

Had this review been written only a year or two ago, lead in petrol would have been a far more controversial subject than it is now, the difference being due to the recent rapid advances in the use of unleaded petrol. It is still, however an important topic and merits discussion.

Lead enters the body through either the mouth, with things eaten or drunk, or breathed in through the nose. Far more lead is likely to be ingested than inhaled, but ingested lead is less well absorbed than that which is inhaled. The rate of absorption also depends on its chemical composition, the volatile organic lead compounds added to petrol being more readily absorbed than the inorganic particulate products of combustion. Poisoning by lead at high concentration has been recognised for a very long time and has been most thoroughly studied. The most common form of lead poisoning seen today is the disturbance of the gastro-intestinal system known as lead colic, accompanying the pain of which will be symptoms such as excessive tiredness, continued headaches, loss of appetite, nausea, and muscular pains. It has been reported by Kehoe (1968) that no cases of such lead poisoning have been known to occur when the blood lead levels were below 80 μg per 100ml of blood. This is far greater than the levels measured, for example by a team sponsored by the British Government who carried out a considerable programme of measurement of atmospheric and blood lead levels in Birmingham, England, around a motorway interchange at a place called Gravelly Hill (Department of the Environment, 1978). They reported blood maxima of 35 μg per 100ml for school children and adults (though most were much lower), excluding only a lead worker whose level was 62 μg per 100ml. They also reported, however, that 'undoubtedly the presence of the motorway interchange results in an increase in the local concentrations' (of atmospheric lead, from about 1 μg/m³ to between 2 and 3 μg/m³).

It is in the possible effects of such marginal increases that the uncertainty lies. A Working Party appointed by the British Government reported in 1980 (DHSS, 1980) that "in the vast majority of the population airborne lead, including that derived from petrol, is usually a minor contribution to the body burden''. They went on to argue that despite being unable to come to clear conclusions concerning the effects of small amounts of lead on the intelligence, behaviour and performance of children, nevertheless Government and industry should take steps ''by which emissions of lead into the air...are progressively reduced''.

This very muted approach was directly contrary to that of others, such as the Conservation Society Pollution Working Party who published a report (undated) after that of the Government's Working Party. This maintained that the earlier report had seriously underestimated the contribution to blood lead levels of directly inhaled airborne lead, and noted the earlier report's findings that ''some 90 per cent of airborne lead comes from lead petrol additives''. They went on to place great emphasis on possible hazards to children, including unborn infants, particularly with regard to intelligence.

This split in medical and scientific opinion has been echoed elsewhere, with the balance of opinion (Walsh, 1988) emphasising the dangers and the need for the removal of lead from petrol at the fastest practicable rate. This now appears to be happening worldwide, and will not be reversed. The UK Department of the Environment has for several years been co-ordinating a programme of surveys to investigate changes in blood level concentrations. Preliminary results (Department of the Environment, 1986, 1987a, 1987b) for 1986 show average falls from 1985 levels of around 10 per cent for adults, 18 per cent for police officers, and 16 per cent for children - not all, of course, due to reductions in the lead content of petrol.

4.1.5   Polycyclic hydrocarbons (PAH)

The contribution made by vehicles to the PAH concentrations in the Birmingham area was estimated by Colwill et al (1984). They found vehicles to be responsible for 92 per cent of PAH near the Midlands Motorway Interchange, 67 per cent in the city centre and 53 per cent in a suburban area.

As with many of the constituent pollutants there is much disagreement between experts as to the extent of the health damage caused by polycyclic hydrocarbons. Whilst there is no doubt that they have a carcinogenic effect, and that they commonly occur in smoke from the incomplete combustion of hydrocarbon fuels of all kinds, there is doubt about whether the concentrations breathed in with air polluted by vehicle exhausts are high enough to produce harmful effects.

For example in a private communication to the author, R E Waller of the Technology and Environmental Health Division of the Department of Health said ''although there have been claims that the general rise in lung cancer might be linked with a new factor in the environment, such as fumes from diesel vehicles, close inspection of the trends does not support any such case, and all definitive studies point to the overwhelming role of cigarette smoking''. He quotes studies of London Transport employees, some of whom are exposed to high concentrations of diesel fumes, and similar studies in the USA, in support of this argument.

However Waller also points out that "the greater efficiency of the diesel engine leads to smaller emissions (of PAH) than from unregulated petrol engines" and his conclusions might not be applicable where the preponderance of the PAH's is from such petrol engine exhausts. Back in 1971, Coffin (Coffin, 1971) had argued that whilst smoking must assume the major blame for the increase of pulmonary cancer, "air pollution may be responsible for an appreciable proportion of the total number of lung cancer cases".

4.1.6   Smoke

A special feature of the diesel engine is its liability to produce black smoke, which is almost pure carbon. As such it has no specific toxic properties, but it does act as a nucleus to carry other products of partial combustion, such as PAH's which produce, as stated previously, carcinogenic activity.

In the 1960's, Waller *et al.* (1965) studied the smoke and PAH contributions in a busy street in London, and the results (Table 4.6) show the large contribution made to smoke by the diesel traffic and also the contributions to PAH by petrol and diesel traffic. Since that date the British Government's Clean Air Act has reduced concentrations from background sources, mainly coal fires, but the traffic sources remain.

TABLE 4.6

Annual mean concentrations of smoke and PAH's in Fleet Street, 1962-63

	Centre of Fleet Street	Mean Background	Traffic Contributions
Smoke, g/m^3	430	143	287
PAH's, ng/m^3			
Benzo(a)pyrene	39	23	16
Benzo(e)pyrene	26	14	12
Benzo(ghi)perylene	46	14	32
Coronene	20	4	16
Anthanthrene	6	2	4

4.2   Subjective effects

Traffic 'fumes' may be visible in the form of smoke, or may be sensed by smell. A substantial part of the emission, however, is not detectable by the senses, and this includes lead and carbon monoxide. A survey (Morton-Williams *et al.*, 1978) gave some valuable insight into subjective attitudes in relation to exhaust emission. As one would expect, only a small minority (7 per cent) claimed to notice traffic fumes when they were indoors at home, although not surprisingly virtually all those who did were disturbed by them. Fumes were stated to be a very much bigger nuisance when out-of-doors, no less than 54 per cent claiming to notice them and 47 per cent finding them a nuisance. Although slightly fewer people were disturbed by fumes than by noise when out-of-doors, it was fumes that tended to evoke stronger responses.

Road traffic is of course not the only source of fumes. About a quarter of those interviewed said there were other kinds of fumes in the area, only about one-third of people describing the air in their district as 'very clean and fresh'. However, the widespread anxiety about possible effects of traffic fumes on people is illustrated by the fact that almost 60 per cent thought that they did in fact have a harmful effect. Table 4.7 shows what such harmful effects were considered to be.

TABLE 4.7

Public opinions concerning possible harmful effects of traffic fumes

Effect	On people generally (per cent)	On respondent personally (per cent)
Cause chest complaints, bad for chest	33	4
Are poisonous, make sick, can kill	11	4
Affect breathing	8	4
Cause cancer	6	0
Affect throat, cause coughs	5	5
Miscellaneous effects	6	5
Others	7	5
No effect	38	74
Don't know	6	5

An interesting insight into the confusion that exists between health effects and subjective effects is provided by the fact that the lorry was considered to be the worst offender in relation to fumes, with buses and coaches coming next. (The precise figures for 'vehicles giving out the worst fumes' were: lorries, 37 per cent; buses and coaches, 13 per cent; cars, 3 per cent; and motorcycles and mopeds, 1 per cent.) This is despite the facts that the same respondents claimed to be particularly worried about health effects; and that almost all the lorries and buses would have diesel engines that emit no lead at all and less carbon monoxide than petrol engines. Clearly, attention is drawn to the emission from these vehicles by their smoke and smell (and their noise, vibration and so on) and it is assumed - erroneously, as it happens - that the emissions are particularly harmful.

75

Excessive, and visible, smoke is always inexcusable and is the result of bad engine maintenance. Odour, however, is a more difficult problem. No single component is responsible for exhaust odour, and complex synergisms undoubtedly occur. Hydrocarbons are responsible for a considerable part of the odour, and oxygen-containing materials may also contribute. Compounds of sulphur and nitrogen can smell strongly although the sulphur contents of exhaust are generally so low that they are present but not detected. The concentration at which a material in the atmosphere is detected by people varies greatly from compound to compound and a list of these 'odour thresholds' for some materials is given in Table 4.8.

TABLE 4.8

Odour thresholds of possible exhaust components

Material	Odour threshold level (ppm)
Hydrocarbons	
Benzene	4.7
Cyclohexane	300
Styrene	0.05
Toluene	2.1
o-Xylene	0.2
p-Xylene	0.5
Oxygen containing compounds	
Acetaldehyde	0.2
Acetone	100
Acrolein	0.2
p-Cresol	0.001
Formaldehyde	1.0
Phenol	0.05
Sulphur containing compound	
Dimethylsulphide	0.001

One of the major problems in assessing odour levels is that of collecting organic materials from the atmosphere in a form suitable for subsequent identification.

As a result, a literature survey produced in 1989 (Ashdown Environmental Limited, 1989) stated that ''very few investigations of odours in roadside environments have been reported. Those that have show that toluene and benzene are the predominant organic compounds present and that petrol engined vehicles emit higher proportions of the lower C_6 - C_9 benzenoids. Diesel vehicles, however, emit greater quantities of the more malodorous higher benzenoids, indanes and napthalenes. Studies of odorous components of roadside air have shown that concentrations of several compounds are likely to exceed the odour detection threshold, for a substantial part of the day, along busy streets.''

This survey drew the conclusion that ''there is no basis yet available for deciding at what level of a particular vehicle pollutant subjective effects become important''. It went on to advocate more research in this field, which might lead to a suitable index and presumably an appropriate standard for the index. This has been a hard enough task in the area of traffic noise, but it seems very doubtful whether it has much chance of success in an area governed by reactions against not only nuisance problems but also health problems, real or imagined, from materials some of which are not detectable by human senses. Attitudes are also strongly influenced at the present time by perceived effects of exhaust emissions on those broader ecological problems that will be discussed in the next section.

4.3 Ecological effects

The ecological effects of exhaust emissions will be considered, for convenience, under four broad headings; the first concerning highly localised lesser effects upon roadside vegetation; the second ozone; and the other two concerning more widespread effects such as their contribution to what are now commonly known as ''acid rain'' and the ''greenhouse'' effect. It should be repeated, however, that this division is somewhat artificial, because these matters are very much inter-related.

4.3.1 Roadside pollution

Vegetation close to a heavily trafficked road is subjected to high concentrations of airborne pollutants, but very few studies have been made of the effects of this. It is still the case that probably the most complete discussion of this matter was provided by an international symposium held in the UK (TRRL, 1979) in 1979, sponsored jointly by the British Ecological Society and the Transport and Road Research Laboratory. This has been summarised fairly fully elsewhere (Watkins, 1981) and only a brief summary is called for here.

As far as lead is concerned, high levels of lead in the soil are of much greater significance to plant life than heavy foliar contamination since much greater quantities of lead can be taken up into plant tissues via the roots than via the leaves. However, even with the high petrol lead levels of 1974, measurements made on the M4 motorway in the UK in that year showed that levels of lead in the soil fell rapidly with distance from the edge of the road (Bevan et al., 1974). Figure 4.1 shows this clearly, and for comparison Figure 4.2 shows the way that atmospheric concentrations fell much more slowly with increasing distance. Consequently it appeared that serious damage by lead would be limited to central reservations and the 0-5m zone closest to the busiest roads and motorways, and this will itself rapidly reduce as more petrol becomes lower in lead content.

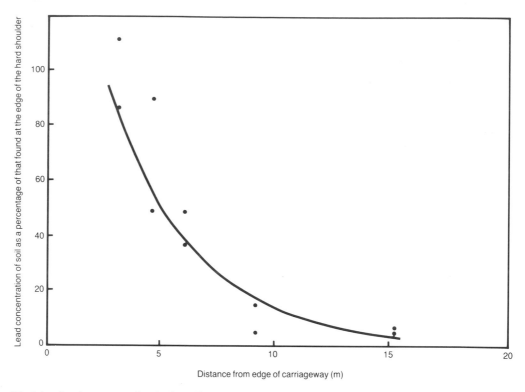

Fig 4.1   Lead concentration in the soil at various distances from the road

Roadside pollution by particulates is apparent to the casual observer, where vegetation becomes darkened and looks dusty as a result of particulate fall-out, probably the majority of which comes from diesel exhausts. This can cause the plants to absorb increased radiant energy, which can influence their net photosynthesis and productivity.

Exposure to high levels of NO_x can cause severe injury to plants, but most reported experiments in this area have employed concentrations that could only be found as far as road traffic is concerned along the very busiest roads. Tomatoes, for example, are very sensitive, and have been found to suffer at road-side concentrations - but one would imagine that few are grown in such situations. The effects on these and other plants appear to be of similar magnitude whether the NO_x is primarily NO or NO_2, but responses of different species are very variable. Probably the most damaging consequence of NO_x from exhaust emissions in this respect arises from its contribution to the production of ozone, and this will be discussed later.

Roadside vegetation must, of course, be included with all other vegetation in any consideration of world-wide effects of air pollution, but meanwhile in the short-term the UK has experienced a relatively luxuriant roadside growth, particularly of the taller growing herbaceous plants. This results, not from changes in exhaust emissions, but from the fact that many roadsides that used to be sprayed regularly with herbicides, or cut more frequently than was really necessary, now do not receive these treatments at

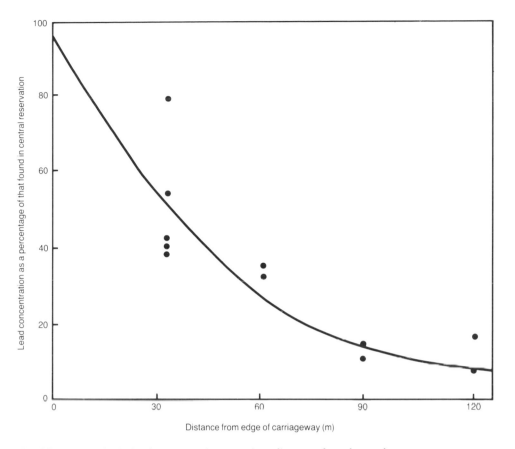

Fig 4.2   Atmospheric lead concentration at various distances from the road

all - or at the most, very infrequently. So long as such growth does not create hazards by, for example, intercepting drivers' lines of sight this is wholly advantageous.

Concern has also been expressed about the possible effects of road surface run-off on water quality. Colwill et al (1984) summarised information available for urban areas and reported measurements in a rural catchment beside the M1 Motorway in Bedfordshire. They found that salt used for de-icing was the most concentrated contaminant in winter run-off. They also estimated total annual yields of suspended solids, lead, oil and PAH and observed the relationships between levels of contamination and rainfall events.

4.3.2   Ozone and PAN (Peroxyacetyl nitrate)

O_3 is unique among gaseous pollutants in that it occurs over large rural areas at concentrations sufficient to damage plants. Although ozone has been known about for over a century, it was not until the 1940's that its environmental implications began to be realised. There are no significant emissions of ozone directly into the atmosphere, all the ozone found there being formed by chemical reactions in the air (Morton-Williams,

1978). Ozone and PAN, but principally ozone, are formed by a series of photochemical reactions from nitrogen oxides and hydrocarbons, emitted partly from vehicle exhausts. This has been discussed earlier in this Chapter.

Plant species vary greatly in their sensitivity to ozone; spinach, beans, clover and lucerne being very sensitive, whilst cabbage, lettuce and sprouts are rather tolerant. Sensitivity is also dependent on other environmental conditions. Plants tend, for example, to be less sensitive when light intensities are low, when humidity is low, and when water supply is restricted. The most sensitive known plant is the tobacco cultivar Bel-W3 which can be injured by hourly mean ozone concentrations above 40ppb, whereas visible injury on other relatively sensitive species may require exposure to concentrations of 100ppb for several hours. When exposure is maintained for several weeks the required concentration for visible damage can be much reduced. A long-term study (Ashmore, 1984) in southern England showed growth reduction in periods when the average maximum hourly mean concentration exceeded 40ppb, or when an hourly mean concentration of 60ppb was exceeded on at least 10 per cent of days.

There have been suggestions (Umweltbundesamt, undated) that ozone is a major factor contributing to the decline of forest health which has affected the Federal Republic of Germany and other countries in Central Europe in recent years. Mean ozone concentrations measured in some of the German forests are as high as those in the USA where it is reasonably certain that such damage is due to ozone, for example in the San Bernadino forest in southern California where ozone has caused extensive damage to the ponderosa pine in recent years. Some of the damage in California is thought to arise through altered sensitivity of the trees to other biotic and abiotic stresses rather than through a direct effect of the gas. The complexity of the relationships involved make it impossible as yet to define a dose-response relationship or to state the threshold concentration of ozone for effects on natural ecosystems. Some concentration figures have been given in section 4.1.3 of this review.

Studies of the effects of ozone on forest health by the UK Forestry Commission (Innes, 1987) have so far been inconclusive. They recognise the "decline in forests that has been observed there (ie in the European mainland) over the last few years, that the area affected has increased, and that both conifers and broadleaves are now affected". They maintain that "one of the most likely explanations is a multiple stress hypothesis involving air pollution as an inciting or predisposing stress, adverse soil conditions as a predisposing stress and short-term climatic factors as inciting stresses". They do, however, conclude by saying "although adverse weather conditions may have triggered the decline, it seems probable that this decline would not have occurred if trees had not already been weakened by air pollution or some other stress".

Despite the public disagreements between official bodies and environmental pressure groups on these matters, to the present author these statements by the Forestry Commission, although expressed with understandable caution, do not seem a world apart from those of the Friends of the Earth (House of Commons Select Committee on the Environment, 1988) "both NO_x and unburnt hydrocarbons are ozone precursors, and whilst the relationship is complex, computer models do exist for predicting the likely impact of changing levels of NO_x and HC on atmospheric ozone levels. Ozone has been implicated as a contributory factor to the forest damage witnessed in central Europe, it has many implications for human health, and may well affect commercial crop production''.

4.3.3 Acidity, 'acid rain'

The main precursors of acid deposition (Buckley-Golder, 1984) are sulphur dioxide (SO_2) and nitrogen oxides (NO_x) emitted into the atmosphere from both natural and man-made sources. The vehicle contribution is mostly of NO_x. Over half a million tonnes is emitted in the UK every year (this total appears recently to have been reducing slightly, but it is very difficult to provide a reliable estimate), and about one-third of this comes from vehicle emissions; the largest amount, and most of the SO_2, comes from power stations. However the NO_x may influence the rates of photochemical oxidation of both SO_2 and NO_x, so that ultimately changes in the quantities of SO_2 and/or NO_x are unlikely to lead to direct proportional changes in the deposition of acidity at a given location. Hydrocarbons emitted into the atmosphere can, in the presence of oxides and oxides of nitrogen, take part in photochemical reactions yielding a range of noxious species including ozone, NO_2, aldehydes, PAN and aerosol species. Thus although hydrocarbons themselves do not contribute to acid deposition they are involved in the production of species that do.

Acidification has been occurring at an accelerated rate in industrialised areas since the Industrial Revolution, and although the tall-stack policy in the UK led to decreasing pollution in urban areas it may well have spread the same pollution farther afield. In addition to this emissions from vehicles have grown rapidly in recent years.

Acidity in soil or water is measured by the pH unit, which is a logarithmic function of the concentration of hydrogen ions. A value of 7pH is considered acidically neutral; less than 7 is increasingly acidic and over 7 is increasingly alkaline. Pure rainwater might be thought to be neutral, but is in fact always slightly acidic even when unpolluted by man: de-ionised water in equilibrium with the CO_2 in the atmosphere has a pH of 5.6, and trace gases that are always present can cause a further lowering of the normal pH to about 5, or even 4.5 (Carlson, 1982).

However studies of rainwater in the UK (UK Review Group on Acid Rain, 1983) have shown a pH as low as 4.1 in south-east England. Measurements around Glasgow (Dolland et al., 1983) showed pH values of 4.26, and 30 per cent of this acidity was said to be of local origin. The largest impacts of acidity have been found in parts of Cumbria and Scotland, where acid deposition was of the same order as in the high impact areas of Scandinavia and North America.

Fog and mist droplets have been found (Waldman et al., 1982) to exhibit pH values of 3.50 and as low as 3.35 in the UK, and 3.2 to 4.2 in the Adirondacks, in the USA.

Many attempts have been made to examine and quantify trends in acid precipitation, such as that for the UK Review Group (UK Review Group on Acid Rain, 1983), but usually without a great deal of success. The problem is complicated by other factors such as changes in weather patterns; changes in sampling and analytical techniques; changes in industrial and urban development and so on. Some studies however have suggested patterns. For example, the nitrate aerosol content of the atmosphere at Chilton in Oxfordshire, UK, has apparently increased by a factor of 3 since 1957 (Salmon *et al.*, 1977) and appears to be linked to increasing quantities of NO_x emitted from low level sources, particularly from motor vehicles. Glaciers and continental ice-sheets preserve the precipitation that has fallen on them over many centuries, and that which fell before the Industrial Revolution generally has a pH over 5. Ice cores studied in Greenland (Herron, 1982) have been found to have concentrations of sulphate and nitrate ions in the ice approximately twice the pre-1900 values, whereas in the Antarctic, which is more remote from man-made sources, changes were barely detectable. Generally there is no reliable way of estimating how much of these increases has been caused by the various sources of pollutants.

The damage attributed to acidity in the environment includes effects on vegetation, aquatic life, structural materials and human health. So far as damage to vegetation is concerned, much of this has been to do with trees. In 1982 it was estimated that about 560,000 hectares of forest in West Germany showed damage, some 8 per cent of the total afforested area. Some workers (Ulrich *et al.*, 1980) attribute this to the consequences of acid deposition, whilst others point to the ozone problems discussed previously. It appears to be most likely that this damage is not caused everywhere by the same factor, but that all is either caused or made worse by some aspect or aspects of pollution acting separately or in combination.

Loss or depletion of fresh-water fish stocks has been reported in several countries of western Europe, notably Scandinavia, Scotland and most recently Wales. 700 lakes in southern Norway had lost their fish population since the 1940's (Wright, 1978) and 65 per cent of these lakes had a pH less than 5. In Wales, trout are now absent from the more acid forest-draining streams of the upper Tywi, although here and in other similar cases the acidification might be due more to increased afforestation than to air pollution, since afforestation of a catchment, particularly with coniferous trees, enhances the acidification and the aluminium content of the water system.

Some man-made emissions from local sources cause accelerated corrosion of metal and enhanced weathering of stonework in urban areas, but this is mostly attributable to SO_2 and is consequently not of great importance in a consideration of vehicle exhaust emissions. NO_x and ozone might influence corrosion, but no quantitative information has been found.

Acid water can dissolve metals from the soil, from piping systems and from tanks - indeed this is one of the sources of lead problems where lead pipes are used. However, except where lead and other metals such as aluminium and copper can be dissolved in large quantities the UNECE has reported (UNECE, 1982) that the data available about acid drinking water suggest no immediate threat to public health. This is, however, an area of concern that merits further attention.

4.3.4   The 'greenhouse' effect

Our planet is made habitable by the presence of certain gases in the atmosphere which trap long wave radiation (Mitchell, 1988). This produces a global mean temperature of 15°C, whereas if the atmosphere did not exist the global mean temperature would be about -18°C. This phenomenon is popularly known as the 'greenhouse effect', and, as these temperatures indicate, the balance is rather delicate.

The most important greenhouse gas is water vapour, but there has been a substantial and increasing effect due to carbon dioxide, with smaller contributions from ozone, nitrous oxide and methane. These are highly relevant to exhaust emissions, whereas the chlorofluorocarbons (CFC's) about which there has recently been much public concern are not, although they have recently been added in large quantities. It is estimated that increased concentrations of all these gases since the mid 19th century has raised global mean temperatures by about 0.5°C, and the projected concentrations, unless action is taken to reduce them, could produce a further warming of about 1.5°C in the next 40 years.

CO_2 is the greenhouse gas emitted in the largest quantity by vehicles. A single tank of petrol produces more than 100kg of CO_2 when burned; motor vehicles provide almost 15 per cent of the world's total CO_2 emissions at the present time (WHO, 1981); and these emissions are set to increase rather than to decrease, while CO_2 produced by industrial processes is declining. Overall, CO_2 concentrations are currently increasing at the rate of 1.5ppm (0.48 per cent) per year, and the concentration in the year 2035, it has been estimated (Ramanathan *et al.*, 1985), will rise from just over 400 ppm to about 475ppm, further enhancing tropospheric/surface heating. The problem here for vehicle interests is that CO_2 is actually a product of good combustion, not bad. The only method available to reduce these emissions therefore is to burn less fuel oil, which means using either fewer vehicles, or vehicles more economical with fuel, or totally different power sources, or some combination of these.

Emission of carbon monoxide (CO) may also be important for climate modification. The reason for this is that highly reactive hydroxyl radicals (OH) which scavenge many anthropogenic and natural trace gases from the atmosphere are themselves used in the oxidation of CO. Thus the increase in CO that is taking place can increase the concentration of several other greenhouse gases such as O_3, CH_4, and NO.

The effect of O_3 is difficult to predict owing to the fact that tropospheric ozone tends to warm the earth's surface through the greenhouse effect, whilst stratospheric ozone has the opposite effect due to the absorption of ultra-violet (short-wave) radiation.

There is at the present time much uncertainty about what effects this global warming will have if it is allowed to continue. These uncertainties arise particularly from inadequate knowledge of climate sensitivity - such as cloud formation and effect; the extent to which the oceans will slow the warming; and the inherent variability of the earth's climate on a timescale of several decades. However, that harmful changes will occur if present trends continue is not in doubt; the only doubts are about when and where they will occur and their overall size.

4.4 Chapter 4 References

ASHDOWN ENVIRONMENTAL LIMITED, (1989) Perceived nuisance of vehicle exhaust emissions - A literature review. Unpublished contractor's report to TRRL.

ASHMORE, M R, (1984) The effects of ozone on vegetation in the United Kingdom, Ozone (ed. P. Grennfelt) IVL, Goteborg.

BEARD, R R and G A WERTHEIM, (1967) Behavioural impairment associated with small doses of carbon monoxide. Am. J. Public Health, 57 (11) 2012-22.

BEVAN, M G, D M COLWILL and L E HOGBIN, (1974) Measurements of particulate lead on the M4 Motorway at Harlington. TRRL Report LR 626. Transport and Road Research Laboratory, Crowthorne.

BUCKLEY-GOLDER, DEBORAH H, (1984) Acidity in the environment. Energy Technology Support Unit, Harwell. Department of Energy.

CARLSON, R J and H RODHE, (1982) Factors controlling the acidity of natural rainwater. Nature, 295, 683-685.

COFFIN, D L, (1971) Health aspects of airborne polycyclic hydrocarbons. U.S. Society of Automotive Engineers, Medical Aspects of Air Pollution, New York.

COLWILL, D M, C J PETERS and R PERRY, (1984) Water quality of motorway run-off. TRRL Report SR823. Transport and Road Research Laboratory, Crowthorne.

CONSERVATION SOCIETY POLLUTION WORKING PARTY, (Undated) Lead or health, Conservation Society, London.

DEPARTMENT OF THE ENVIRONMENT, (1978) Lead pollution in Birmingham, Pollution Paper No 14, HMSO, London.

DEPARTMENT OF THE ENVIRONMENT, (1986) Pollution Report No 22, Digest No 8. London.

DEPARTMENT OF THE ENVIRONMENT, (1987a) Pollution Report No 24. Digest No 8. London.

DEPARTMENT OF THE ENVIRONMENT, (1987b) News Release 223. London.

DEPARTMENT OF HEALTH AND SOCIAL SECURITY, (1980) Lead and health, Report of a Working Party on Lead in the Environment. HMSO, London.

DOLLAND, C J, M H UNSWORTH and M J HARVEY, (1983) Pollutant transfer in upland regions by occult precipitation. Nature 302, 241-242.

ELLER, B M, (1977) Impurity Sources of F, CI, NO$_3$ and SO$_4$ in Greenland and Antarctic precipitation. Journal of Geophysical Research, 87, 3052-3060.

HERRON, M M, (1982) Impurity sources of F, CI, NO3 and SO4 in Greenland and Antarctic precipitation. Journal of Geophysical Research, 87, 3052-3060.

HOUSE OF COMMONS SELECT COMMITTEE ON THE ENVIRONMENT, (1988) Inquiry into air pollution, memorandum submitted by the Friends of the Earth. London.

INNES, J L and R C BOSWELL, (1987) Air pollution and forestry, Forest Health Survey Parts 1 and 2, Bulletins 70, 74 and 79, Forestry Commission, HMSO, London.

KEHOE, R A, (1968) Lead intake from food and the atmosphere, Science, 159.

MITCHELL, J F B, (1988) The ''greenhouse'' effect and climate change. Meterological Office, Dynamical Climatology, Technical Note No 70.

MORTON-WILLIAMS, J, B HEDGES and E FERNANDO (1978). Road traffic and the environment. Social and Community Planning Research, London.

RAMANATHAN V. R J CICERONE, M B SINGH and J T KIEHL, (1985) Trace gas trends and their potential role in climate change. Journal of Geophysical Research, 90, 5547-5566.

SALMON L D, H F ATKINS, E M R FISHER, C HEALY and D V LAW, (1977) Retrospective trend analysis of the content of UK air particulate material 1957-1974, AERE - R8680.

SCHULTE, J H, (1963) Effects of mild carbon monoxide intoxication. Arch. Eng. Health, 7 524-30.

TRANSPORT AND ROAD RESEARCH LABORATORY, (1979) The impact of road traffic on plants. TRRL Report SR513, Transport and Road Research Laboratory, Crowthorne

UK REVIEW GROUP ON ACID RAIN, (1983) Acid Deposition in the United Kingdom, Warren Spring Laboratory.

ULRICH, B, R MAYER and P K KHANNA, (1980) Chemical changes due to acid precipitation in a Loess-derived Soil in Central Europe. Soil Science, 130, 193 199.

UMWELTBUNDESAMT, (undated) Monatsberichte aus dem Messnetz, UBA, Berlin.

UNECE, (1982) Effects of sulphur compounds and other pollutants on health. ENV/IEB/R14. Geneva.

UNITED KINGDOM PHOTOCHEMICAL OXIDANTS REVIEW GROUP, (1987) Interim report, ozone in the United Kingdom. Department of the Environment. London.

WALDMAN, J M, J W MUNGER, D J JACOB, R C FLAGAN, J J MORGAN and M R HOFFMAN, (1982) Chemical composition of acid fog. Science, 218, 677-680.

WALLER R E, B T CUMMINS and P J LAWTHER, (1965) Air pollution in a city street. Brit. J. Ind. Med. 22, 128-138.

WALSH, M P, (1988) Background Report on Vehicles. Ministerial conference on Transport and Environment.

WATKINS, L H, (1981) Environmental impact of roads and traffic. Applied Science Publishers.

WHO, (1981) Environmental health criteria No 13, carbon monoxide. WHO, Geneva.

WHO, (1979) Environmental health criteria No 7, photochemical oxidants, WHO, Geneva.

WRIGHT, R F and E SNEKVIK, (1978) Acid precipitation: chemistry and fish populations in 700 lakes in Southernmost Norway. Verh. Internat. Verein Limnol 70, 765-775.

5 Emission control technology

Vehicle designers have many different objectives to achieve, all of which are ultimately concerned with the marketability of their product. To judge from current advertising in the United Kingdom it would seem to be the perceived wisdom of manufacturers that public requirements for cars are mainly for high performance as measured by maximum speed and maximum acceleration. After these come comfort, safety in accidents and mechanical reliability, and after that - and until recently nowhere at all - environmental characteristics including the quality of exhaust emissions. With the present emphasis on low lead fuel this has changed, but mostly only in respect of lead. For commercial vehicles emphasis is put on load-carrying capacity and economics of operation.

There are, however, indications that times may be changing. Some countries, such as the Federal Republic of Germany, are using fiscal means to encourage the purchase of low emission cars, and in the United Kingdom this method has been employed to encourage the use of low lead petrol. Some countries appear not to need this; in Denmark, for example, there has been a substantial demand for cars equipped with catalysts without any legislation or tax incentive.

The problem of carbon dioxide and its relevance to the 'greenhouse effect' introduces a new problem since CO_2 is a product of good combustion and is produced in direct proportion to the amount of fuel burnt. Steps to minimise products of poor combustion must naturally tend to increase its emission over that achievable if vehicles are optimised for fuel economy only. Reduction of CO_2 emission can only be achieved by reducing the amount of fossil fuel burnt, and this matter has now become of international concern.

This Chapter will discuss firstly current vehicles, then alternative developments and fuels, and in each case both petrol and diesel engines must be considered and the costs of technology must be taken into account.

5.1 Current vehicles (petrol engines)

5.1.1 Basic engine modifications (Hickman, 1989)

As has been discussed in Section 2.5 the two main factors governing the formation of pollutants within the petrol engine are the composition of the air and fuel mixture and the timing of its ignition. The air:fuel ratio has a very marked effect (Felger, 1987) (Figure 5.1). If there is too little oxygen, combustion is incomplete and high levels of carbon monoxide and hydrocarbons are produced. These are much reduced at higher air: fuel

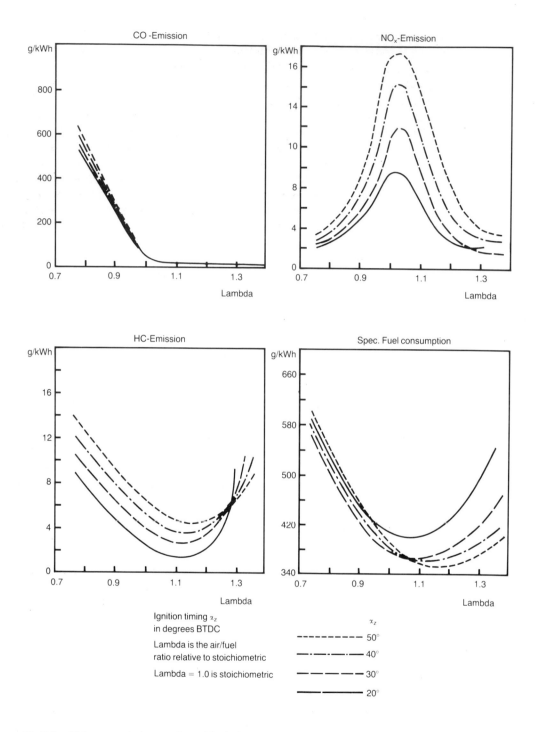

Fig 5.1 Exhaust emissions and specific fuel consumption - influence of air ratio lambda and ignition timing (Source: Felger)

88

ratios when there is sufficient oxygen available for complete combustion. However, as the combustion becomes more efficient, the combustion temperature increases, resulting in greatly increased formation of oxides of nitrogen. The air: fuel ratio at which there is exactly the correct amount of air to combine with all the fuel is called the stoichiometric ratio, and has a numerical value of about 14.7:1. A further increase in air: fuel ratio, providing an excess of air, reduces the cylinder temperature and production of oxides of nitrogen falls. At very high air: fuel ratios hydrocarbon emissions increase because of the increased tendency for either total misfire or partial burning under the more difficult conditions for combustion.

Air: fuel ratio is also defined in terms of the unit "lambda" (λ) which has a value of 1.0 at the stoichiometric ratio of 14.7:1. Values higher than 1.0 represent weak mixtures and vice-versa.

The ignition timing influences the formation of oxides of nitrogen and hydrocarbons by varying the cylinder temperature profiles. Retarded ignition results in lower peak temperatures and higher exhaust temperatures than advanced timing. The formation of oxides of nitrogen is reduced because of the lower peak temperatures and the higher exhaust temperatures promote more complete oxidation of residual hydrocarbons.

The optimization of the processes of air and fuel metering, mixing and ignition is an important step in the production of a low-emission engine. The rapid development of the electronics and microcomputer industry has made significant improvements possible. The conventional combination of carburettor and distributive ignition system can now be replaced by fuel injection and electronic ignition equipment of varying complexity to provide much more precise control of these important functions. Figure 5.2 is a schematic diagram of a modern engine management system (Lucas HighLine). In addition to many other functions, a microprocessor controls the engine's fuel and ignition systems in accordance with the operation of the vehicle and a stored engine map that specifies optimum conditions for the full range of engine speed and load settings.

Advances have also been made in the design of engines. The inlet manifold design, the size, number and geometry of the valves and the shape and configuration of the cylinder are of great importance in determining the efficiency of the fuel mixing and combustion. The internal cylinder design strongly influences hydrocarbon emissions: crevices and surfaces retain fuel and oil that escape burning. The design and materials used for the cylinder head determine its thermal properties. Thus, for example, aluminium engines generally operate at lower combustion temperatures and produce less oxides of nitrogen.

Exhaust gas recirculation (EGR) is another common means of reducing the formation of oxides of nitrogen. The addition of a proportion of inert exhaust gas to the air/fuel charge is an effective way of reducing the peak cylinder temperature by increasing the mass of gas to be heated by a given mass of petrol.

Hydrocarbons and carbon monoxide can be oxidised by mixing additional air with the hot exhaust gases as they leave the engine. This can be done by the 'pulse air' system in which a valve admits air into the exhaust manifold near to the exhaust valve under the

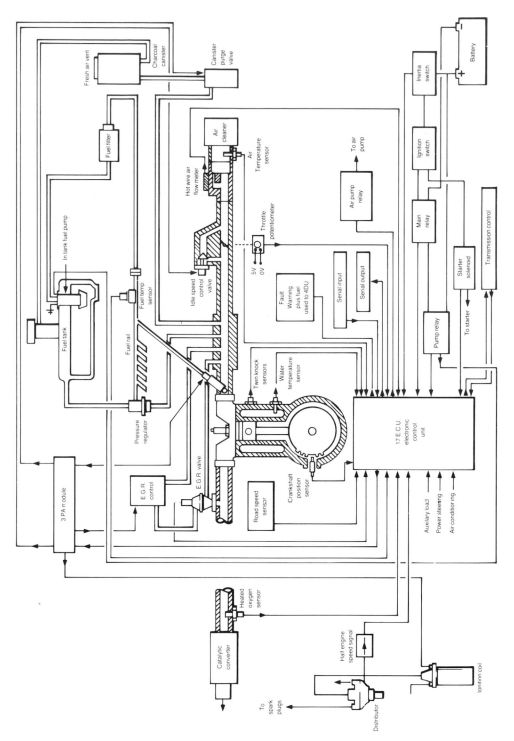

Fig 5.2   An example of an engine management system

influence of the pressure changes in the manifold. It is also possible to use 'thermal reactors' which are essentially chambers in the exhaust manifold in which the oxidation reactions take place, and into which air is pumped and high temperatures can be maintained by lagging.

5.1.2 Catalytic converters

Catalytic converters have been in use for many years to control exhaust emissions. The catalyst consists of a ceramic support matrix, a washcoat, usually of aluminium oxide, that provides a very large surface area and a surface layer of precious metals that perform the catalytic function. The most commonly used metals are platinum, rhodium and palladium. Their proportions are chosen to provide the required performance from the catalyst: platinum and palladium have good carbon monoxide and hydrocarbon oxidation activity while rhodium is effective for the reduction of nitric oxide. The catalyst, in a stainless steel container, forms part of the vehicle's exhaust system. For a catalyst to operate effectively, the temperature must exceed the 'light-off' value (typically 300°C, which in normal urban driving takes 1-3 minutes to achieve) and the exhaust gas composition must be suitable. They can be used in three configurations, as oxidation, twin-bed or three-way catalysts.

Oxidation catalysts In the presence of oxygen, an oxidation catalyst promotes the conversion of carbon monoxide and hydrocarbons to carbon dioxide and water. Thus, provided an air: fuel ratio greater than stoichiometric (ie a weaker mixture) is maintained to ensure residual air in the exhaust, an oxidation catalyst will substantially decrease these pollutants whilst marginally increasing carbon dioxide.

Twin-bed catalysts This configuration consists of a reduction catalyst, where oxides of nitrogen are converted to nitrogen, followed by an oxidation catalyst. The reduction catalyst requires an oxygen-free exhaust mixture which is achieved by controlling the air: fuel ratio below stoichiometric. Additional air is injected after the reduction catalyst to provide the oxygen needed by the oxidation catalyst.

Three-way catalysts Three-way catalysts have superseded both oxidation and twin-bed catalysts for most vehicle applications. They are able to oxidise carbon monoxide and hydrocarbons and, at the same time, reduce oxides of nitrogen. This is achieved by careful control of the air: fuel ratio and, therefore, of the exhaust gas composition. When a vehicle is operated with a stoichiometric air: fuel ratio, it is possible to cause all the oxidising agents in the exhaust to react with all the reducing agents, resulting in the elimination of both by their conversion to carbon dioxide, water and nitrogen. The air: fuel ratio range for efficient operation is very narrow (Hodgson, 1987) (Figure 5.3) and good fuel and engine management systems are therefore needed to give maximum conversion.

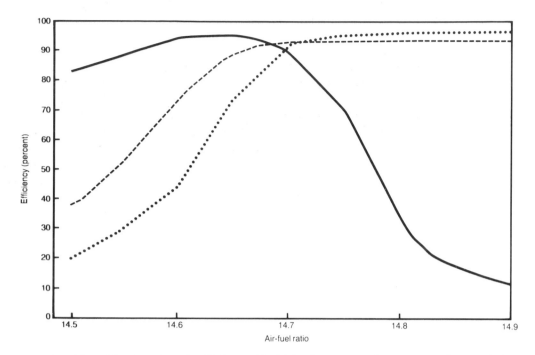

Fig 5.3   Effect of the air-ratio on the efficiency with which a three way catalyst converts exhaust emissions

5.1.3   Relative effectiveness of emission control technologies

There are inevitably advantages and disadvantages inherent in the use of different methods of controlling emission rates. Presently, a three way catalyst fitted to the exhaust of an engine with full control of fuel injection and ignition can provide the greatest reduction of emissions and, because of the much more exact control of the fuelling necessary with a catalyst, the fuel efficiency will improve relative to an automobile with a less controlled engine. The Australian Environmental Protection Agency (undated) estimated a saving of 5-10 per cent based on US and Japanese experience and tests conducted in Australia. Even so, because it is constrained to operate by air: fuel ratios very near to stoichiometric, its application does not permit the additional fuel saving advantages of operating vehicles using lean mixtures. Further-more, all catalysts are susceptible to poisoning by lead and by the phosphorous that is present in most engine oils. While it is perfectly feasible to eliminate these from the fuel and oil, and many countries now actively promote the use of unleaded petrol, experi-ence in the USA has shown misfuelling to be a serious problem. Doubts have also been expressed concerning the physical durability of catalysts in Europe where some national speed limits are considerably higher than in the USA or Japan. Tests (Pearce and Dvies, 1990; Evans and Wilkins, 1985) in the UK have suggested that this is unlikely to be a serious problem.

With current technology, engine modifications alone are not able to reduce emissions as much as with a three way catalyst. Such modifications are not, however, susceptible to the potential problems of catalysts discussed above. Engines without exhaust catalysts may be tuned for better fuel economy because fuelling rates are not restricted to satisfy a catalyst's requirements and misfuelling is unimportant.

In a recent study to examine the proposed integration of an extra-urban high speed driving cycle into the EEC test procedure, the Committee of Common Market Motor Manufacturers (CCMC) carried out exhaust emission tests on a wide variety of vehicles equipped with a range of emission control systems. Their results provide a useful comparison of the capabilities of different techniques for controlling emission rates and are summarised in Figures 5.4 to 5.6. The results shown are for cars driven over a test comprising a full, cold start ECE Regulation 15 urban test followed immediately by a high-speed extra-urban cycle. Although the test cycles are very stylized, they were based on an analysis of real driving patterns to give representative average speeds, rates of acceleration and relative durations for the various parts of the test. The results therefore give a good approximation of emission rates during normal, mixed-mode driving. The reduced emission levels from vehicles fitted with controlled three-way catalysts are apparent.

5.1.4 Evaporative emissions

Evaporative emissions of hydrocarbons occur whenever fuel is exposed to the atmosphere. There are four major sources of evaporative emissions:

Fuelling emissions in which the vapour occupying the space above the fuel remaining in the tank is displaced into the atmosphere during refuelling.

Running losses in which hydrocarbons evaporate from the vehicle's fuel system while it is still in use.

Hot soak losses in which fuel evaporates from the fuel system of a warmed-up vehicle after it has been stopped.

Diurnal losses which occur because of the action of diurnal temperature variations on the fuel and vapour in the fuel tank.

In a review of volatile organic emissions in Western Europe (CONCAWE, 1987), it was estimated that evaporative emissions were responsible for 1.19 million tonnes of the annual total of 3.69 million tonnes of hydrocarbon emissions from petrol engined vehicles in 1983. Their relative importance will increase as more stringent exhaust emission controls take effect.

In systems for reducing evaporative emissions, vapour vented from the fuel system is channelled to a storage area and subsequently to the engine where it is burnt with the fuel/air mixture. The storage area may be the crankcase or, more commonly, a canister containing activated charcoal onto which the vapour is absorbed. Figure 5.7 shows schematic representations of evaporative emission control systems. Tests carried out by

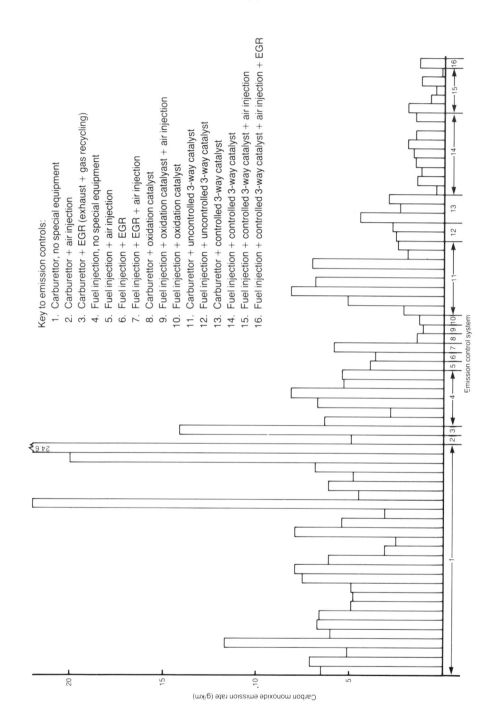

Key to emission controls:

1. Carburettor, no special equipment
2. Carburettor + air injection
3. Carburettor + EGR (exhaust + gas recycling)
4. Fuel injection, no special equipment
5. Fuel injection + air injection
6. Fuel injection + EGR
7. Fuel injection + EGR + air injection
8. Carburettor + oxidation catalyst
9. Fuel injection + oxidation catalyast + air injection
10. Fuel injection + oxidation catalyst
11. Carburettor + uncontrolled 3-way catalyst
12. Fuel injection + uncontrolled 3-way catalyst
13. Carburettor + controlled 3-way catalyst
14. Fuel injection + controlled 3-way catalyst
15. Fuel injection + controlled 3-way catalyst + air injection
16. Fuel injection + controlled 3-way catalyst + air injection + EGR

Fig 5.4   The carbon monoxide emission rates for cars with various emission control systems
(Source: CCMC)

94

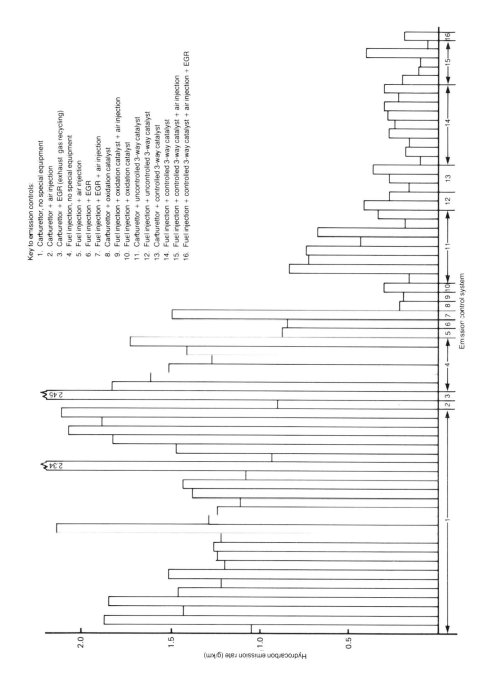

Key to emission controls:

1. Carburettor, no special equipment
2. Carburettor + air injection
3. Carburettor + EGR (exhaust gas recycling)
4. Fuel injection, no special equipment
5. Fuel injection + air injection
6. Fuel injection + EGR
7. Fuel injection + EGR + air injection
8. Carburettor + oxidation catalyst
9. Fuel injection + oxidation catalyst + air injection
10. Fuel injection + oxidation catalyst
11. Carburettor + uncontrolled 3-way catalyst
12. Fuel injection + uncontrolled 3-way catalyst
13. Carburettor + controlled 3-way catalyst
14. Fuel injection + controlled 3-way catalyst
15. Fuel injection + controlled 3-way catalyst + air injection
16. Fuel injection + controlled 3-way catalyst + air injection + EGR

Fig 5.5   The hydrocarbon emission rates for cars with various emission control systems
(Source: CCMC)

95

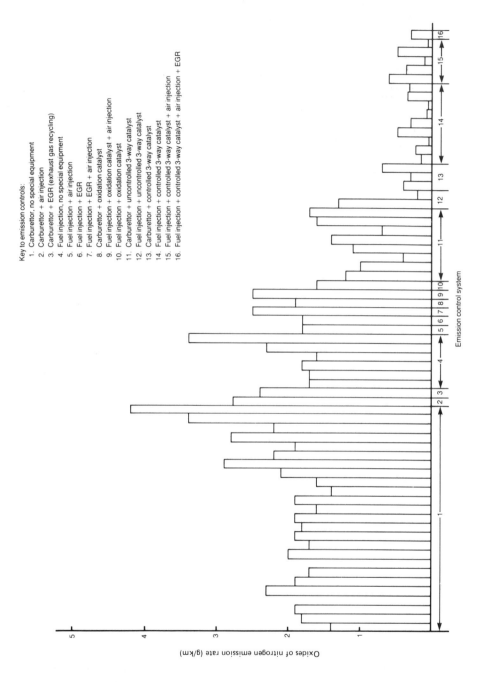

Key to emission controls:
  1. Carburettor, no special equipment
  2. Carburettor + air injection
  3. Carburettor + EGR (exhaust gas recycling)
  4. Fuel injection, no special equipment
  5. Fuel injection + air injection
  6. Fuel injection + EGR
  7. Fuel injection + EGR + air injection
  8. Carburettor + oxidation catalyst
  9. Fuel injection + oxidation catalyst + air injection
  10. Fuel injection + oxidation catalyst
  11. Carburettor + uncontrolled 3-way catalyst
  12. Fuel injection + uncontrolled 3-way catalyst
  13. Carburettor + controlled 3-way catalyst
  14. Fuel injection + controlled 3-way catalyst
  15. Fuel injection + controlled 3-way catalyst + air injection
  16. Fuel injection + controlled 3-way catalyst + air injection + EGR

Emission control system

Oxides of nitrogen emission rate (g/km)

Fig 5.6   *The oxides of nitrogen emission rates for cars with various emission control systems*
(Source: CCMC)

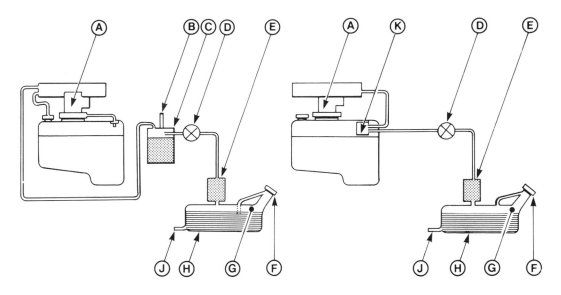

Evaporative emission systems

The carbon canister system

A – Internally vented carburettor
B – Canister vent
C – Carbon canister
D – Three-way control valve
E – Fuel/vapour separator
F – Non-vented filler cap
G – Expansion void
H – Fuel tank
J – Fuel line connection

The crankcase storage system

A – Internally vented carburettor
D – Three-way control valve
E – Fuel/vapour separator
F Non-vented filler cap
G – Expansion void
H – Fuel tank
J – Fuel line connection
K – PCV valve

*Fig 5.7   Schematic drawings of two types of evaporative emission control systems
(Source: Ford Motor Company, 1981)*

CONCAWE (1987) showed control systems based on carbon canisters to achieve a reduction of more than 90 per cent.

5.1.5   Lead

The control of lead emissions is now achieved in many countries by reducing or eliminating lead additives from petrol (see Section 2.5.8). An alternative method, the use of an exhaust filter, to trap lead compounds was tested in the early 1970's (Colwill, 1974). The trap was found to reduce emissions by about 40 per cent overall but there was considerable variation for different types of vehicle and driving conditions. Under some conditions, particularly in the transition from urban to high-speed driving, some of the lead collected on the trap could be purged into the atmosphere. Furthermore, it was found not to be possible to regenerate a used trap and careful disposal procedures would be needed.

5.1.6   Fuel consumption

For obvious economic reasons and increasingly because of concern over emissions of carbon dioxide, it is important that vehicle fuel consumption be kept to the minimum consistent with their satisfactory performance. Many of the techniques used to control exhaust emissions also have a direct effect on fuel consumption.

Some of the effects of exhaust emission control techniques on fuel consumption are discussed above. Table 5.1 (Commission of the European Communities, 1983) summarises these effects more quantitatively. The base case is taken to be a conventional engine with a carburettor and mechanical ignition system. Fuel consumption changes are given as a percentage relative to the base case for a number of possible, more advanced configurations. The changes indicated are often relatively broad ranges, reflecting uncertainties, vehicle to vehicle variations and variations that might result from differing design criteria such as performance, emissions and economy for which the vehicle may be optimised.

TABLE 5.1

The effects of various exhaust emission control technologies on the fuel consumption of petrol engined cars

Engine / vehicle modifications	Change in fuel consumption (a) from base case (percent)
Electronic ignition system	-3 to -6
Full engine management	-3 to -10
Air injection	+7 to 0
Air injection + EGR	+19 to 0
Electronic ignition + EGR	+2 to -4
Lean burn (b) (carburettor)	-4 to -20
Lean burn (fuel injection)	-15 to -22
Lean burn (carburettor) + EGR	-3 to -13
Air injection + oxidation catalyst	0
Air injection + EGR + oxidation catalyst	+27 to 0
Lean burn (carburettor) + oxidation catalyst	-13
Controlled 3-way catalyst	+16 to -5

Notes:
(a) Changes are relative to the base case of a conventional engine with a carburettor and mechanical ignition.
(b) Lean burn engines will be discussed later in this Chapter.

5.1.7 Costs

Exhaust emission controls. The cost to the consumer of implementing tighter emission control standards has three components: (i) the increased cost of the vehicle, including the cost of additional or more advanced components and the costs to the manufacturer for development, production and profit; (ii) the increased costs for maintaining the vehicle and (iii) the cost of additional fuel if the vehicle's fuel economy is worsened by the emission control measures. In some cases the changes can give financial gains to the consumer, as when fuel economy improves and maintenance costs reduce as a result of improved engine design. Table 5.2 shows a compilation prepared for the EC commission (Commission of the European Communities, 1987) of the costs of various low emission vehicle configurations.

The ranges shown in the Table are quite large, but they are bound to be unless one is considering a specific type of vehicle. They do however enable broad comparisons to be made of different systems.

Lead controls. The production and use of unleaded petrol imposes a number of direct and indirect additional costs on the motorist. Increased investment by oil companies in refinery plant is needed, their operating costs increase, and distribution costs are temporarily higher because of the present need to segregate leaded and unleaded petrol and the additional facilities needed to supply both simultaneously. More crude oil is used to produce unleaded petrol, and because of the vehicle changes needed to enable operation using unleaded petrol, there are also costs to the motor manufacturing industry.

The cost implications of several strategies for reducing or eliminating lead from petrol were assessed in 1984 by the ERGA II group set up by the Commission of the European Communities. Their findings are summarised in Tables 5.3 to 5.5 for a number of alternative assumptions (Cases A to E) about the types of fuel available - note that Case A limits the lead content to 0.15 g/l, a limit subsequently adopted and applying to curent leaded petrol.

From Table 5.5 one can estimate costs to consumers thus: a car costing £10,000 initially running on leaded petrol would cost £67 more if built to use lead-free 94 octane; it would have reduced maintenance costs of just a few pounds a year; and its fuel would cost (not counting taxation charges) about £13 more a year. This increase in fuel costs only occurs if the extra cost of producing a lead-free fuel is passed on to the motorist. In some countries (UK, Germany), where fiscal means are employed to encourage its use, the lower level of tax can reduce the fuel costs to the user.

Evaporative emissions. Costs of evaporative emission controls were estimated by the UK Department of Transport in 1986. The cost of equipping a vehicle with a control system was estimated to be £52 (approximately $875 million for the UK fleet). Additional national costs for the modifications needed by petrol filling stations were, (i) to reduce emissions during vehicle refuelling, £435 million plus £8 million/year increased maintenance costs and (ii) to reduce emissions during bulk refilling of petrol storage tanks, £24 million plus £0.7 million/year maintenance.

TABLE 5.2

The costs to consumers of various emission control technologies

Engine modifications	Change in cost from base case (%)*		
	Purchase	*Maintenance*	*Fuel economy (+ worse) (- better)*
Electronic ignition system	0.4 to 4	0 to 3.5	-3 to -6
Full engine management	1 to 10	0 to 8	-3 to -10
Air injection	0.5 to 3.4	-	+7 to 0
Air injection + EGR	1 to 5.5	-	+19 to 0
Electronic ignition + EGR	3 to 5	0 to 6	+2 to -4
Lean burn (carburettor)	1 to 5	0 to 4	-4 to -20
Lean burn (fuel injection)	7	7.5	-15 to -22
Lean burn (carburettor) + EGR	1.7 to 8.6	7.5	-3 to -13
Air injection + oxidation catalyst	1.7 to 6	-	0
Air injection + EGR + oxidation catalyst	4 to 15	-	+27 to 0
Lean burn (carburettor) + oxidation catalyst	10	11	-13
Controlled 3-way catalyst	4.4 to 15	-	+16 to -5

Source: Commission of the European Communities (1983)
* Base case comparison is a conventional engine with carburettor and mechanical ignition

TABLE 5.3

Costs of lead-free petrol for the vehicle manufacturing industry, EEC countries

	Case A	Case B	Case C	Case D	Case E
Lead level g/l	0.15	0	0	0	0
Fuel octane numbers available RON	92/98	92	94	96	92/96
% of gasoline pool (Regular/Premium)	25/75	100	100	100	25/75
Lead time (years) from adoption of directive	0	5-6	5-6	5-6	3-4
Total vehicle manufacturing industry investment (US $M (1983))	0	640	430	230	230
Minimum additional cost of new cars %	0	1.0	0.67	0.35	0.35
Fuel consumption CEP* = 1.0	0	4.5	2.5	0.6	1.5
deterioration % = 1.5	0	7.0	4.0	1.0	2.2
Reduction in vehicle maintenance costs	0	1.2-2.6	1.2-2.6	1.2-2.6	1.2-2.6
Number of vehicle types for recertification	0	1048	693	672	N.A
Certificates	0	1800	2240	2160	N.A

CEP* is the elasticity of fuel consumption with octane number:
CEP = (% increase in fuel consumption)/(units reduction in octane number)

Source: Commission of the European Communities (1984)

TABLE 5.4

Costs of lead-free petrol to the oil industry

	Case A	Case B	Case C	Case D	Case E
Lead level g/l	0.15	0	0	0	0
Fuel octane numbers available RON	92/98	92	94	96	92/96
% of gasoline pool (Regular/Premium)	25/75	100	100	100	25/75
Lead time (years) from adoption of directive	4	X	X	X	X
Oil industry investment $/tonne annual gasoline production for constant mileage	14.3	24-38	25-39	33-57	26-45
Extra energy, tonnes crude oil/1000 tonne gasoline for constant mileage	22	57	45	53	45
Additional cost, $/tonne gasoline for constant mileage	12.1	19.7	18.9	24.5	20.3
Total investment in EEC, $M	1,200-2,500	1,500-2,200	2,100-3,200	2,800-4,800	2,200-3,800
Change in aromatics, % by volume	+3	+6	+7	+10	+9
Change in benzine, % by volume	+ 0.1	+ 0.4	+ 0.7	+ 1.0	+ 0.8

Notes.
All costs are $ US at 1983 levels.
Production assumed 85M Tonnes/year in all cases
 Change from 0.4g/l to 0.15 g/l lead involves no penalties
x Impossible to define on an EEC basis
Source: Commission of European Communities (1984)

TABLE 5.5

Costs of lead-free petrol to consumers   EEC countries

	Case A	Case B	Case C	Case D	Case E
Lead level g/l	0.15	0	0	0	0
Fuel octane numbers available, RON	92/98	92	94	96	92/96
% of gasoline pool (Regular/Premium)	25/75	100	100	100	25/75
Minimum additional cost of new cars %	0	1.0	0.67	0.35	<0.35
Reduced maintenance costs/vehicle year $ US 1983	0	1.2-2.6	1.2-2.6	1.2-2.6	1.2-2.6
Additional cost(a) of fuel/ vehicle year $ US 1983 (CEP = 1)(b)	13.4	22.0	21.5	27.6	22.8

(a) not counting taxation differences
(b) CEP - see note under Table 5.3

Source: Commission of the European Communities (1984)

5.2   Current vehicles (diesel engines)

5.2.1   Engine design

Diesel engines operate at air: fuel ratios far higher than petrol engines and, consequently, because of the ready availability of excess oxygen, produce less carbon monoxide and hydrocarbons. Indeed, carbon monoxide is produced in such small quantities that levels rarely approach legislated maximum values and no special control techniques are needed. In order for complete combustion, even in the oxidising environment of a diesel engine, it is necessary for the fuel to be evaporated, thoroughly mixed with the air and to be at a high enough temperature. Inevitably, because of inhomogeneity of the fuel spray, incomplete mixing, cooling and deposition on relatively cold surfaces such as the cylinder walls, some fuel is not burnt and is emitted in the exhaust. Substantial quantities of hydrocarbons can be emitted under cold start

103

conditions. The formation of oxides of nitrogen depends on the temperature, pressure, availability of oxygen and the duration, during the combustion cycle, of conditions that promote their formation. In general, oxides of nitrogen emission rates are broadly comparable with those of petrol engines.

Diesel engines produce more smoke and particulates than petrol engines. Because of differences in mixture preparation, there is considerably less time for mixing before ignition in a diesel engine than in a petrol engine. Particles of carbon are produced in fuel rich zones and subsequently absorb unburnt hydrocarbons and other organic compounds. Smoke, measured optically, represents primarily the carbon particles while particulates measured by mass include all non-gaseous emissions.

A number of diesel exhaust components are not specifically regulated but there is growing concern that they are harmful or undesirable. They include polycyclic aromatic hydrocarbons and nitro-polycyclic aromatic hydrocarbons, some of which are known carcinogens; organic oxygen-containing compounds, mainly aldehydes and ketones, which are major contributors to the malodour of diesel exhaust; and sulphur dioxide derived from the sulphur present in diesel fuel. Lead is not added to diesel fuel. Diesel fuel is much less volatile than petrol and evaporative emissions are therefore not important.

5.2.2   Basic engine modifications

The design of a low emission diesel engine is very much a compromise. Most of the methods for reducing particulate and hydrocarbon emissions improve the combustion efficiency and are fuel efficient but result in higher levels of oxides of nitrogen in the exhaust. An example is shown in Figure 5.8 in which smoke, emissions of oxides of nitrogen and fuel consumption are shown as functions of injection timing and fuel pumping rate (Tonkin and Etheridge, 1987). As the injection timing and pumping rate are varied, the smoke emission rate and fuel consumption follow quite similar trends which are opposite to the trend in oxides of nitrogen emission rate. Thus, if reduced emissions of all components are required, it is often necessary to offset potential improvements in one direction to provide the required performance in another. In practice, this may involve the use of a combination of emission reducing techniques whose interactions may be complex and sometimes opposite in effect. For example, turbocharging tends to increase the formation of oxides of nitrogen but it may be applied to a previously naturally aspirated engine to maintain power output and limit smoke emissions when injection retard is used to reduce oxides of nitrogen emissions. Turbocharging also tends to reduce noise.

The more common techniques available for controlling emission rates are discussed below. Much of this information is based on two reviews of the feasibility of reducing diesel emissions (Commission of the European Communities, 1983; Tonkin and Etheridge, 1987). The second of these was commissioned from Ricardo Consulting Engineers by TRRL, and has been summarised by Latham and Tonkin (1988).

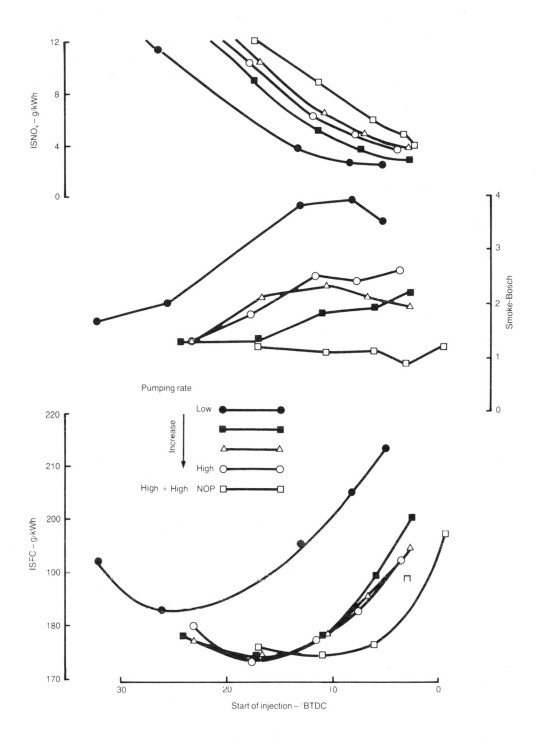

*Fig 5.8   Effect of injection rate on smoke and NOx emissions for a heavy duty
direct injection diesel engine
(Source: Tonkin and Etheridge, 1987)*

Optimization of the combustion process   Efficient combustion, with the resulting low emissions of hydrocarbons and smoke, can be achieved if the air and fuel are thoroughly mixed. Important design considerations are the shapes of the cylinders, pistons and induction ports, which determine the level of swirl and turbulence of the fuel/air mixture in the cylinder, and the fuel injection systems. High pressure fuel injection systems, with more precise, possibly electronic, control of fuelling levels and timing, combined with well designed combustion chambers, can provide a good basic engine that is amenable to further improvement using other techniques.

Turbocharging and charge cooling   Turbocharging and charge cooling are methods of increasing the power output of an engine by increasing the mass of air input to the engine and therefore allowing more fuel to be burnt. Turbochargers increase the air pressure of the air supplied to the cylinders while charge coolers reduce its temperature and therefore increase its density. Turbochargers are used independently but charge coolers are used only with turbocharged engines. The influence of these processes on emission rates is varied. Turbocharging tends to increase oxides of nitrogen and reduce particulates. At light loads, highly turbocharged and turbocharged/charge cooled engines may misfire because of the high air: fuel ratio, resulting in increased hydrocarbon and particulate emissions. By reducing the peak cycle temperatures and pressures, charge cooling directly reduces oxides of nitrogen emissions.

Injection retard   Retarding the injection timing is the most effective way of reducing oxides of nitrogen emissions because it reduces peak temperatures and pressures during combustion. Unfortunately, though, injection retard increases fuel consumption, smoke and hydrocarbon emissions, particularly under light load conditions (Figure 5.9 (Tonkin and Etheridge, 1987)). Emissions of oxides of nitrogen at light loads are, however, naturally low and it is possible to use a variable timing regime to give more advanced injections during light load operations for smoke and hydrocarbon control without producing significantly worse oxides of nitrogen emissions. Such a flexible timing plan would require an electronically controlled fuel pump.

Exhaust gas recirculation (EGR).   Replacing some of the intake air with exhaust gas has the dual effect of reducing the cycle temperature and the available oxygen. Both effects reduce oxides of nitrogen formation and increase hydrocarbon and particulate emissions. There are a number of problems in applying EGR to diesel engines. Engine durability is reported to be poorer because of contamination of the lubricating oil by exhaust particulates. EGR systems for turbocharged engines must overcome the adverse pressure differential between inlet and exhaust, implying either the use of an additional pump or introduction of the exhaust via the turbocharger with the consequent risk of blockage or damage by exhaust particulates. The gains in nitrogen oxides control are often outweighed by increases in hydrocarbon and particulate emissions: Figure 5.10 shows (Hollis, 1984) that an EGR rate of 30 percent achieved a 50 percent reduction of oxides of nitrogen but that particulate emissions doubled.

Fuel injection equipment.   High hydrocarbon emission levels can result from deficiencies of the fuel injection equipment. Secondary (or tertiary or multiple) injections of fuel can occur if pressure pulses in the high pressure fuel lines are high enough to reopen the injectors. Because these injections occur late in the cycle the fuel is not burnt efficiently

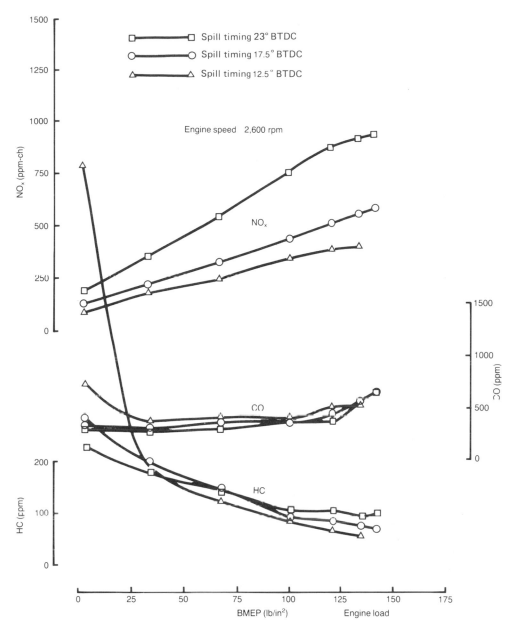

Fig 5.9   The effects of injection retardation and engine load on exhaust emission rates for a heavy duty
direct injection diesel engine with turbocharging and charge cooling
(Source: Tonkin and Etheridge, 1987)

and very high hydrocarbon levels are emitted. Poor combustion also results if fuel is deposited on the walls of the combustion chamber. A further source of hydrocarbon emissions is the fuel retained in orifices of the injector. This can be blown or evaporated from the injector during the low pressure part of the cycle and pass through the engine unburnt. These problems can be overcome by well designed injection systems with optimised delivery valves and high pressure lines and a well-matched combustion bowl

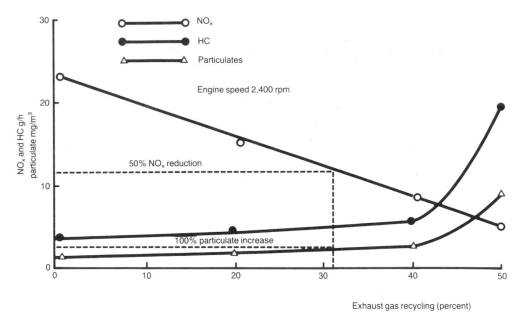

Fig 5.10 The effect of exhaust gas recycling on exhaust emissions from a light duty
indirect injection diesel engine at part load
(Source: Hollis, 1984)

and injection system incorporating low volume nozzles. This type of attention to design is a cost effective way of reducing hydrocarbon emissions.

Lubricating oil control. A significant proportion of hydrocarbon and particulate emissions is derived from the lubricating oil that can enter the engine via the piston rings, valve guides or turbocharger. The use of improved piston rings and the fitting of valve stem seals can be very beneficial (Tonkin and Etheridge, 1987). Unburnt oil can contribute 30 to 40 percent of particulate mass emissions from engines operated over the US Heavy Duty Transient Cycle. A comparison of emissions from an engine before and after valve stem seals were fitted showed hydrocarbon levels to fall by about 50 per cent (Hollis, 1984).

5.2.3   Effects of fuel composition

Many of the properties of diesel fuel significantly influence exhaust emission rates. A summary of these and other effects of fuel composition (Hollis, 1984) is given in Table 5.6 and some of the more important parameters are discussed below. In many cases, it is possible to re-optimise an engine for operation using a fuel with properties considerably different to those of the fuel for which it was designed. For that reason, it may be that the geographical and temporal consistency of diesel fuel supplies is more important than the absolute quality.

Cetane number. The cetane number determines the time delay between the start of fuel injection and the onset of combustion. If the delay time is long, with a low cetane fuel,

TABLE 5.6

General effects of fuel characteristics on Diesel engine operation

	Reduced cetane number	Reduced volatility	Increased aromatic content	Increased viscosity	Increased density
Cold starting	Worse	Worse		Better	
White smoke	<	>			
Black smoke		<	<	<	<
Power				<	<
Fuel consumption					>*
Noise	<				
Rate of pressure rise	<				
HC emissions	<	>	<		
CO emissions	<	<			
NO$_x$ emissions	<	>	<		
Odour	<	>			
Combustion deposits		>		<	
Piston lacquering	<	>		<	
Nozzle coking				<	
Injection characteristic				Changes	

Symbols: < Increases   > Reduces   * measured volumetrically

Source: Hollis 1984.

the subsequent combustion proceeds at a higher rate because of increased vaporization of the fuel. As a result, there is a tendency for hydrocarbons and smoke to increase because of the less efficient combustion. Oxides of nitrogen emissions are likely to be only slightly increased since the late start and increased rate of combustion have opposite effects. Additives can be used to improve cetane numbers. Organic nitrates such as hexyl nitrate, cyclohexyl nitrate and octyl nitrate can be used in low quantities (typically 0.1 percent by volume) to give an improvement of the order of 5 cetane numbers. The influence of cetane number on emissions is the same whether the fuel is enhanced by a cetane improver or is of high initial quality.

Physical properties - volatility, viscosity and density. Fuel delivery and combustion are influenced by these properties. They are interrelated and, in general, a poor quality fuel would be more viscous, more dense and less volatile than a premium diesel. Combustion would be poorer and overfuelling could result from high density fuels. Fuel consumption on a mass basis and smoke emissions would increase while oxides of nitrogen could be reduced. Injection systems can be reset for engines to operate more efficiently using poorer quality fuels.

Aromatic content. The proportion of aromatic hydrocarbons in the fuel significantly affects the rates of exhaust emissions. Figure 5.11 shows increases (Barry *et al.*, 1985) in particulate, hydrocarbon and oxides of nitrogen emissions as the aromatic content increases. Furthermore, the formation of polycyclic aromatic hydrocarbons and the odour intensity of diesel exhaust are linked to the aromatic content of the fuel. The modification of refinery practices to produce fuels containing less aromatics is the only way to restrict their basic influence on rates and types of emission although the emissions are amenable to control using the engineering methods described above.

Sulphur content. Diesel fuels contain substantial amounts of sulphur (typically 0.15 to 0.5 percent by weight (Institute of Petroleum, 1986). On combustion, the sulphur yields sulphur dioxide, particulate sulphates and a small proportion of sulphur trioxide. Most of these are emitted to the atmosphere and contribute to its burden of acid species. Some, however is retained in the engine and exhaust system where its corrosive nature accelerates wear. The sulphate content of diesel particulate matter is typically 10-15 percent and reductions would therefore assist significantly in reducing total particulate emissions. The effective use of particulate traps (Section 5.2.4) is only possible if low sulphur fuels are used because they rapidly become blocked if sulphate levels are high, and the sulphate is not removed by normal trap regeneration methods. Fuel desulphurization is the only method available for reducing sulphur emissions.

Fuel additives and alternative fuels. Fuel additives have been used to suppress smoke emissions. They are based on barium, calcium or manganese and act as catalysts for the conversion of carbon particles to carbon dioxide. However, involatile inorganic salts of these metals (sulphates and carbonates) are also produced, which contribute to particulate mass emissions and increase the difficulties of using particulate trap systems (see below).

Diesel engines may be designed to operate using a wide variety of fuels. Much research has studied the use of renewable fuels such as alcohols and vegetable oils as alternatives or additives to fuels derived from mineral oil. Particulate emissions from methanol are very low and use of this fuel has been considered as a means of alleviating pollution problems caused by buses operating in urban areas. The California Energy Commission is currently operating over 500 methanol powered buses (Institute of Petroleum, 1986). There are some practical problems with this fuel. Because of the lower heating value and density of methanol the volumetric fuelling rate must be approximately twice that of conventional diesel and therefore fuel pumps and tanks must be larger. Engine wear increases because methanol does not have lubricating properties equal to those of diesel, and methanol corrodes some plastics and aluminium alloys.

5.2.4   Particulate traps

If limits on particulate emissions are very low, it is unlikely that engineering changes alone will enable production engines to comply with them. It is widely believed that the 1991 US requirement (particulate emission limit 0.25 g/bhp.h) may be achieved but that the further reduction to the proposed 1994 US limit of 0.1 g/bhp.h will necessitate the use of exhaust aftertreatment equipment (Freeman, 1989). During the 1980s there has

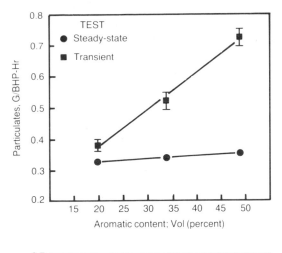

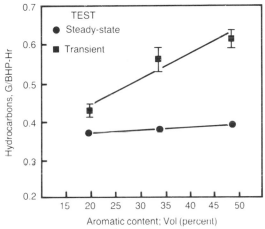

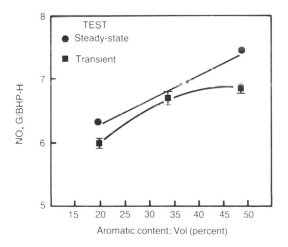

Fig 5.11 The effect of the aromatic content of fuel
on the exhaust emissions from a heavy
duty direct injection diesel engine
(Source: Barry et al, 1985)

111

been a considerable amount of research on methods of trapping exhaust particulates but, to date, no system has been shown to give satisfactory and sustainable performance in service. The majority of traps are filters that retain solid material as the exhaust gas passes through them. An alternative method has been proposed that exploits the fact that exhaust particulates carry a significant electrical charge and can be removed by electrostatic precipitation from the exhaust stream.

Unless a trap is periodically cleaned, it will quickly become blocked by the accumulated particulates and it is the design of effective regeneration techniques that is the main difficulty in producing efficient trap systems. It would be possible, though cumbersome, periodically to remove the particulate from an electrostatic precipitation system manually. However, with the more common filter systems, the particles are embedded in and deposited on the fabric of the filter and must be removed by burning them in situ. In order to burn the particulates, the temperature must be higher than normally experienced in the exhaust system. Two main approaches have been studied: to increase the temperature of the trap or to use catalysts that reduce the ignition temperature to a value within the range normally found. Increased trap temperatures have been achieved by using burner systems (Rao *et al.*, 1985) or electrical heating (Arai *et al.*, 1987). Catalysts may be added to the fuel (Lawson *et al.*, 1985) sprayed separately into the trap (Hardenburg, 1987) or be an integral coating of the filter (Rijkeboer *et al.*, 1986).

There are many practical problems, particularly with regeneration, to be solved before trap systems can reliably be used in vehicles. For example, Hickman and Jaffray (1986) found regeneration of a catalyst coated trap fitted to a bus to be incomplete during normal urban use, so that the burden of particulates in the trap continued to increase. When the bus was tested under more extreme operating conditions, the contents of the trap were purged into the atmosphere, leading to very high particulate emission.

Fuel consumption. Because most diesel engined vehicles are operated commercially and cover very high annual mileages, their fuel economy is of great importance and influences their commercial competitiveness significantly. Fuel economy will almost certainly suffer as a result of severe exhaust emission limits. In particular, the techniques available for reducing oxides of nitrogen emissions (primarily ignition retard and EGR) will lead to poorer economy. Figure 5.12 (Hollis, 1984) shows the relationship between fuel consumption and oxides of nitrogen emissions for typical heavy duty diesel engines. Other engine and vehicle improvements such as increased use of turbocharging and charge cooling, better control of injection rates and timing, use of advanced transmission systems and improved vehicle aerodynamics may offset some of the losses in fuel efficiency.

A further significant increase in fuel consumption would result if particulate traps were widely used. The exhaust back pressure imposed by an efficient filter would result in a loss of engine power which would be more severe if the trap regeneration were not efficient and back pressures increased because of particulate build-up in the trap. Particulate traps could well increase the exhaust back pressure beyond the limit the engine manufacturer is prepared to approve. This could in turn have implications for the warranty for the engine.

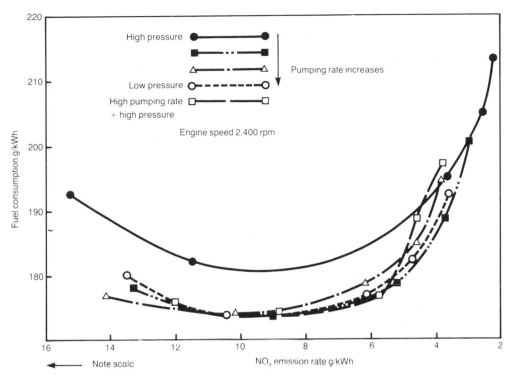

Fig 5.12   Relationship between NOx emissions and fuel consumption for
typical heavy duty diesel engines
(Source: Hollis, 1984)

Table 5.7 shows estimated fuel economy changes associated with a range of exhaust emission requirements the NO_x value of 8 being the base case.

5.2.5   Costs

Vehicle costs are expected to increase where additional equipment (for example, charge coolers or particulate traps) is needed to comply with exhaust emission requirements. The use of alternative, more advanced equipment (such as electronic fuel injection systems or variable geometry turbochargers) will increase costs initially but the increases may be partly offset by the economies of larger scale production when such equipment becomes standard. Increases in vehicle maintenance costs are not anticipated except in association with the use of particulate traps which have not yet been demonstrated to be durable. Tables 5.8 (Tonkin and Etheridge, 1987) and 5.9 show estimated cost increases for individual engine modifications likely to be needed to meet future emissions standards and for engines combining a number of modifications that would be able to comply with a range of possible future emission levels.

In addition to increased vehicle costs, operators would face extra costs resulting from the expected fuel economy changes associated with stringent emission control measures. Table 5.10 analyses the operating costs of heavy duty vehicles in the United Kingdom in 1987 (Transport Engineer, 1987). It can be seen that fuel costs represent

TABLE 5.7

NOx reduction versus particulate and HC plus fuel economy penalties - diesel engines

NOx (g/bhp-h)	Particulates (g/bhp-h)	Hydrocarbons (g/bhp-h)	Fuel Consumption Penalty, %
8	0.4-0.5	0.6-0.8	0
6	0.5-0.7	0.7-1.4	2.5-4
4	0.6-1.0	0.8-1.7	7-12

TABLE 5.8

Cost of diesel engine exhaust emissions control technology

Technology	Estimated extra cost as percentage of engine first cost (excluding development costs)
(a) Baseline engine, no emissions control equipment Developed for performance only	Nil
(b) Injection timing retard	Nil
(c) Low sac volume/VCO nozzles	Minimal
(d) Turbocharging	3-5% (1)
(e) Charge cooling	5-7%
(f) Improved high pressure fuel injection	13-15% (2)
(g) High pressure fuel injection with electronic control	14-16%
(h) Variable geometry turbocharging	1-3% (3)
(i) Particulate trap	5-25% (4)

Notes:
(1) Assumes engine was previously naturally aspirated.
(2) Fuel injection equipment typically represents 25-30% of the engine cost. High pressure systems are expected to be about 50% more expensive and may also require engine modifications to the fuel pump drive train.
(3) Assumes turbocharging was already applied to the engine.
(4) Published information concerning the use of particulate traps shows a wide variation of estimated production costs.

Source: Tonkin and Etheridge (1987)

TABLE 5.9

Estimated cost and time implications of various emission levels for heavy and light diesel engines

HEAVY DUTY DIESEL

Enacted or promulgated legislation		Technological level to meet legislation	Timing impact / Cost impact
Level 1			
	88/77	State of the art today n/a, t/c and t/c l All conform	Available now. 18-24 month lead time. No real cost impact
Level 2			
CO	11.2	n/asp engines no longer competetive. t/c	1st April, 1991 subject to early decision
NOX	10.4	becomes the norm. Fuel cons. penalties	late commitment gives vulnerability
HC	2.0	no major engine design impacts, but increases	cost 10%> level 1 for previously n/a
PART	0.8	required in fuel injection system pressures.	engines, 3-5% extra cost for t/c
Level 3			
As level 2 0ther than HC 1.35		As level 2	Cost and time as level 2
Level 3a			
NOX	8.5	Major changes	1st April 1983
HC	1.35	* Combustion systems	Cost 10% + over levels 2/3
CO	11.2	* Fuel injection systems	more with electronics/
PART	0.6	(High pressure) (Variable timings) * Increasing move to intercooling	
		Some products will need electronic management	
Level 3b and	Level 4	US 1991 Technology equivalent	1st April 1996 cost at least 10%
NOX 9.0	7.0 - 7.5	* vast majority of engines now	increase over level 3a
HC 1.2	1.35	intercooled	
CO 5.0	11.2	* Further increase in electronic management	Also use of intercooling has major
PARTS 0.35	0.34		impact vehicle packaging. Hence cost and time.
		* VG or wastegate turbos now being used * Pie rate control * Major attention required on Lub.oil consumption * Potential use of catalysts and/or traps (this mandates control of fuel sulphur levels)	

LIGHT DUTY DIESELS

	88/77	IDI n/a and t/c Di n/a and t/c Today's State of the Art with or without modulated EGR	IDI lowest cost compared with di + EGR, but latter has significant fuel cons benefit

Source: Society of Motor Manufacturer and Traders, unpublished, 1989

115

TABLE 5.10

Typical Heavy Duty Vehicle Operating Costs

GROSS WEIGHT, TONNES	12	24	38
No of AXLES	2	3	3+ 2 artic
NET COST (£)	15,600	30,900	40,550
ANNUAL MILEAGE	20,000	40,000	50,000
LIFE, YEARS	5	5	7
FUEL CONSUMPTION (m.p.g)	13.9	9.5	7.52
PAYLOAD (tonnes)	7.4	15.8	24.7
STANDING COSTS: (£ per year)			
Overheads	4,318	6,000	8,099
Licence	410	1,610	2,730
Insurance	355	523	830
Depreciation	3,123	4,867	4,735
Interest	1,030	2,039	1,983
Drivers' wages + NIC + subsistence	8,710	12,215	13,530
Standing cost per year	17,946	27,254	31,907
Standing cost per working day of 240 a year	74.77	113.56	132.95
RUNNING COSTS			
Fuel and oil (£1.14/gal)	1,870	4,800	7,580
Tyres	385	1,607	1,904
Maintenance (own)	2,116	3,854	5,485
Running cost p/year (£)	4,371	10,261	14,969
Running cost p/mile (p)	21.85	25.65	29.94
TOTAL COST PER YEAR (£)	22,317	37,515	46,876
TOTAL COST PER MILE (pence)	111.58	93.79	93.75
ECONOMIC VALUE p/tonne-load-mile	15.07	5.94	3.80

Source: Transport Engineer (1987)

approximately 10-20 percent of total costs and therefore deteriorations of fuel economy of the order shown in Table 5.7 could increase overall costs by up to 2 percent.

It is shown above (Section 5.2.3) that fuel composition changes, particularly reductions of the sulphur and aromatic content, could be beneficial for emissions control. Ingham and Warden (1987) and Weaver et al (1986) studied the costs of fuel changes for emission control and concluded that the reduction of sulphur levels was a cost effective option. Indeed, Weaver's analysis indicated that the savings in maintenance costs associated with the use of low sulphur fuels far outweighed the increased refinery costs.

Small (1988) studied the comparative costs of reducing fuel aromatics, using particulate traps and using methanol fuel for reducing particulate emissions from buses. His assumptions and results are summarized in Table 5.11.

5.3   Alternative engines and fuels

Conventional internal combustion engines, either spark ignited petrol engines or compression ignited diesel engines, have dominated the automotive market almost to the exclusion of all others. New engines, including modifications of internal combustion engines, have been studied, but with very few exceptions have not been commercially produced. The objectives of the studies have usually been to develop more efficient and, sometimes incidentally, less polluting power units and to develop engines to use alternatives to petrochemical fuels. The suitability of these engines and the engineering problems that must be overcome before they can be widely used in automotive applications vary, but none is expected seriously to rival current petrol and diesel engines in the near future, as far as operating efficiency and economy are concerned. However the increasing emphasis on lower pollution levels must encourage research and development in this field. Some of the alternatives that have been worked on to the present time are discussed briefly below.

5.3.1   'Lean-burn' engines

The importance of the air-fuel ratio in a petrol engine has been discussed earlier, and the jargon phrase 'lean-burn' merely means an engine that operates on a mixture unusually weak in fuel. If the air: fuel ratio is increased beyond 17:1 the levels of NO_x and CO begin to be reduced, and NO_x is reduced very significantly at a ratio of 20:1.

A disadvantage of the lean-burn engine is that it is operating close to the limit of driveability, particularly under the transient conditions experienced on the road, and mis-fire can occur. This places great demands on the fuel and ignition control systems and on the design of the combustion chamber and inlet valves. One of the most advanced lean-burn engines produced so far (Kobayashi et al., 1984) has very much enriched mixture during idling, acceleration, and high engine speeds to provide adequate performance and this, of course, reduces its ability to limit emissions during

TABLE 5.11

Cost-effectiveness of various measures to reduce exhaust emissions from urban buses

ASSUMPTIONS	Baseline	Fuel Modification	Particulate Traps	Fuel Modification and Particulate Traps	Methanol
Extra vehicle cost					
Capital ($)	0	0	1,100	1,100	5,200
Maintenance ($/yr)	0	0	315	315	582
Fuel quality					
Sulphur (%)	0.05	0.05	0.05	0.05	0.00
Aromatics (%)	28.70	17.00	28.70	17.00	N A
Fuel economy (mi/gal)	3.81	3.81	3.70	3.70	1.81
Fuel price ($/gal)	0.78	0.791	0.78	0.791	0.55
Emissions (g/mi)					
Carbonaceous particulates	6.080	4.256	0.608	0.304	0.304
SO_4	0.026	0.026	0.080	0.080	0.000
SO_2	0.836	0.836	0.809	0.809	0.000
Cost increase per bus ($/yr)		98	674	776	4,638
Total particulates					
Emissions reduction (%)		25.7	76.7	80.9	95.7
Cost-effectiveness ($/kg)		1.58	3.63	3.95	19.98
Incremental cost-effectiveness ($/kg)		1.58	4.65	9.79	107.70
Severity index					
Emissions reduction (%)		18.9	55.4	58.5	96.9
Cost-effectiveness[a]		1.58	3.69	4.02	14.51
Incremental cost-effectiveness[a]		1.58	4.77	9.79	30.53
Mortality index					
Emissions reduction (%)		8.8	24.1	25.6	98.5
Cost-effectiveness[a]		1.58	3.95	4.28	6.65
Incremental cost-effectiveness[a]		1.58	5.30	9.79	7.49
Expected mortality reduction (deaths/yr)		1.28	3.51		14.33
Incremental cost-effectiveness ($/$10^{-6}$ death)		0.34	1.14		1.62

[a]Cost-effectiveness is expressed in dollars per unit reduction in the index [i.e.,in dollars per reduction in pollution that is equivalent (as measured by that index) to 1 kg of particulates].
NOTE: Annual mileage = 34,115; real interest rate = 8.0 percent; bus life = 12 years; and capital recovery factor = 0.1296. NA = not applicable.
Source: Small (1988)

those operations. Lean burn engines may be fitted with oxidation catalysts to control excess CO and HC emissions but, because of the oxidising composition of the exhaust, catalytic reduction of NO_x is not possible. For that reason, further developments are needed before lean burn cars can fully meet the increasingly stringent emission standards being adopted in Europe.

The 'stratified charge' engine is a type of lean burn engine in which the air/fuel charge is not uniformly mixed before ignition. This approach overcomes the combustion and driveability problems associated with lean mixture operation by ensuring that the air: fuel ratio is relatively low at the start of combustion but gets progressively higher as the stroke proceeds, and so still provides the benefits of lower fuel consumption and emissions of carbon monoxide and oxides of nitrogen. Two main types of stratified charge engine have been studied. In the open chamber type, the mixture composition is controlled by the design of the combustion chamber and fuelling systems to provide a relatively rich mixture (near to stoichiometric) at the spark plug that becomes progressively weaker as combustion proceeds. In pre-chamber engines, a stoichiometric air fuel mixture is ignited in a small auxiliary combustion chamber and provides a torch that ignites the much weaker mixture in the main chamber.

Only Honda have built production vehicles with stratified charge engines (of the pre-chamber type). With an oxidation catalyst to control hydrocarbon emissions, their engine has met current US emission limits.

5.3.2 Rotary (Wankel) engines

In a rotary engine, a triangular rotor turns within an elliptical combustion chamber. The tips of the triangle seal against the walls of the chamber and its motion therefore varies the volume of the space between the rotor and chamber wall. Thus, the rotation performs the compression and expansion functions of a piston in a conventional engine. Because the motion produced by the engine is rotational rather than reciprocating there is no requirement for the crank-slider mechanisms used in piston engines. For that reason, rotary engines are simpler, smaller and lighter than piston engines. The major engineering difficulty has been to provide effective and durable seals for the rotor tips. Emissions of carbon monoxide and hydrocarbons from rotary engines are significantly higher than from reciprocating engines because it is difficult to ensure a homogeneous mixture formation in the long, narrow combustion space. Oxides of nitrogen emission levels are similar to those from conventional engines. Production cars with rotary engines have been built by Mazda which require three way catalysts to meet current US emissions standards. Norton produce rotary engined motor cycles.

5.3.3 Gas turbines

A gas turbine engine uses an expanding stream of hot gases to drive a turbine which, via a suitable transmission system, can drive the wheels of a vehicle. Air is drawn into the engine and compressed. It is then mixed with fuel which is burnt and the combustion products drive the turbine. The air is cool when drawn in, is heated by the compression and then mixed with fuel and ignited in the combusion chamber, heating it further and

119

greatly expanding its volume. The volume and temperature of the gases determine the amount of work the engine can provide. Gas turbines are simpler and lighter than piston engines and may, therefore, have advantages over diesel engines for large commercial vehicles. Combustion is continuous and may be controlled to give low rates of emission. There are engineering difficulties in producing durable, lightweight components that can withstand the high temperatures in a gas turbine but advances in materials technology, particularly using ceramics, may help significantly. No production vehicles use gas turbine engines.

5.3.4   Steam engines

Steam engines use the Rankine cycle to drive turbines or pistons in reciprocating engines. Water is heated in a boiler, the steam produced is used to drive the turbine or piston, is condensed and pumped back to the boiler. Steam engines are large and inefficient compared with internal combustion engines and their use is largely restricted to stationary applications and marine propulsion. In common with other external combustion engines, however, they can use a wide range of fuels and can be controlled to produce low emissions.

5.3.5   Stirling engines

In a Stirling engine, a gas passes alternately between two cylinders under the influence of a heating and cooling cycle, driving pistons in the cylinders to provide the work output. The gas is compressed and externally heated in one cylinder, causing a rapid pressure increase. It then expands, driving the pistons, is cooled by the expansion and passage through a heat exchanger to the other cylinder where it is recompressed to restart the cycle. To control the power output, a complicated valve system is used to vary the mass and therefore the pressure of the gas in the engine. Because the heat is supplied by external combustion, a wide range of fuels and configurations can be used and combustion may be controlled to give low rates of emission of pollutants. Stirling engines are large and costly in comparison with internal combustion engines but, theoretically at least, they are more fuel efficient. They can be very quiet, and for that reason they have been used in small numbers in portable generator sets. None has been used in production vehicles. Technically they could replace diesel engines in many heavy commercial vehicles, and would give substantially reduced emissions and noise, but the investment to supersede such a well established technology seems so far to have presented an insuperable barrier.

5.3.6   Alternative fuels

Spark and compression ignition internal combustion engines can be modified to operate on fuels other than petrol and diesel, and studies have been carried out to examine a number of alternatives. Important possibilities include alcohols and vegetable oils whose sources, unlike fossil fuel reserves, are renewable. Hydrogen, natural gas (mainly methane), liquified petroleum gas (LPG, mainly propane and butane) and synthetic liquid fuels derived from the hydrogenation of coal have also been considered.

The motivation for the study of alternative fuels has been the desire to exploit fuel sources other than crude oil. The oil crisis of the early 1970's with the accompanying sharp price increases and concern that reserves were being rapidly depleted gave a considerable impetus to the research. Biomass or alternative fossil fuels are exploited in countries where this is cost-effective. In the Netherlands, natural gas has largely replaced LPG for heating purposes. The resulting surplus is used in cars, and approximately 15 percent of vehicle mileage is by cars using LPG. Brazil actively promotes the use of vegetable-derived ethanol as an alternative fuel. The properties of these fuels with respect to engine design and modification and exhaust pollution are clearly very varied. Hydrogen, methane and methanol burn very efficiently and are intrinsically low polluting fuels. Others, such as vegetable oils, are of poorer combustion quality than petro-chemical fuels and their emissions must be carefully controlled.

A review of literature on the influence of oxygenated fuels (both pure alcohols and blends of petrol and oxygen containing compounds) on the performance and emissions of spark ignition engines was carried out for TRRL by the National Engineering Laboratory (1983). The review and subsequent measurements found that use of these fuels made little difference to the basic regulated emissions but there were small but significant increases in unregulated emissions, particularly aldehydes.

Methane. This is the main constituent of natural gas, and of biogas which is formed from anaerobic decomposition of organic matter. It has the highest resistance to detonation of any fuel and is therefore used in engines with spark ignition rather than compression ignition. Much of the HC emission from spark ignited engines comprises unburnt fuel and hence a high proportion of methane can be expected in the HC emission of a methane burning engine.

Liquid petroleum gas (LPG). LPG is linked with petroleum production, but can also be produced by liquification of butane and propane from natural gas. It consists mainly of butane and propane, and is stored as a pressurised liquid. It is normally fully vapourised before being mixed with air in the induction manifold and hence has a mixing advantage over petrol which enters the cylinder as droplets of fuel. The result is reduced HC, CO and soot emissions due to improved homogeneity. NO_x emissions are at a similar level to those from petrol.

Alcohols (methanol and ethanol). The primary source of methanol is natural gas, but it can be made from coal or from bio-mass by passing CO and hydrogen produced by gasification over a catalyst. Ethanol can be produced by fermentation with yeast of sugar, or of starch converted to sugar by the action of enzymes. The resulting liquor must be distilled (and dehydrated if it is to be mixed with petrol).

Methanol and ethanol have higher octane numbers than petrol, and hence good power output and fuel economy are obtained with spark ignited engines. The high latent heat of vapourisation of alcohols gives the advantage that charge temperatures before combustion are reduced with a consequential reduction in NO_x formation. Homogenous spark ignited operation can be achieved at leaner air: fuel ratios than is possible with petrol, also leading to reductions in NO_x.

In a homogenous spark ignited engine the HC emissions are similar to those from a petrol engine, and alcohols have the disadvantage of producing aldehyde emissions approximately three times as great as those of petrol. They also have a number of handling problems including water absorption, corrosiveness and lubricant incompatibility. Methanol also has an explosion risk and high toxicity, since ingestion of small quantities can be fatal, as can inhalation of high concentrations.

Table 5.12 (provided by Ricardo) gives a useful comparison of the emission of CO_2 - the most important 'greenhouse gas' produced by vehicles - for the alternative fuels discussed so far, based on a car of gross weight 1,000 kg and a typical fuel consumption.

Hydrogen. As a fuel, hydrogen is almost completely free from pollution and consequently a fair amount of development work is proceeding in this field - in the Federal Republic of Germany, (Birch, 1988) for example.

Hydrogen can be produced in quantity by the electrolysis of water. This requires a supply of electricity, but if sufficient could be made available via solar energy, or some other non-polluting source such as wind or wave power, geothermal, or nuclear fusion, the entire process would be free from air pollution in any form barring only a trace amount of NO_x in the vehicle exhaust. Nothing else would be produced other than water vapour.

BMW (Ward's Engine Update, 1989a) has been experimenting with a system which injects cryogenic hydrogen into the combustion chamber which already contains the required charge of air. This has been effectively accomplished in some of the company's 735iL models to give a range of 300 km (186 miles), a supercharger providing a power output at present about 30 per cent below that of the corresponding petrol engine. There

TABLE 5.12

CO_2 emissions from alternative fuels

Fuel	CO_2 per Litre of fuel* (kg/l)	Euromix fuel cons (1000 kg car) (L/100 km)	CO_2 Emissions (G/km)
Petrol ($CH_1.9$)	2.406	7-8	168-192
Diesel ($CH_1.8$)	2.694	5-6	135-162
LPG (Propane)	1.524	8-10	122-152
Butane	1.772	7.5-9.5	133-168
Methanol	1.088	12-15	130-163
Ethanol	1.503	10-12	150-180

*Assumes complete combustion of the fuel

are design problems associated with safety, because hydrogen is a dangerous fuel to handle in its gaseous state, and with the weight and bulk of the necessary storage tank. However in view of the other clear advantages many people look upon hydrogen as being the fuel of choice for the next century (Birch, 1988).

It has, incidentally, been reported that the USSR has already flown a 3-engined TU155 jet airliner with one of the three engines fuelled by liquid hydrogen (Compressed Air Magazine, 1989). The observed flight was said to be quite uneventful except that the hydrogen-powered engine left a particularly noticeable white vapour trail.

Electric motors. Electricity can certainly be regarded as an alternative fuel, and vehicles using battery operated electric motors have been used for many years for special purposes, usually low-speed, local delivery services. They emit no pollution on the road, although if the electricity they use (via storage batteries) is initially generated by power stations burning fossil fuel, they will cause overall air pollution depending upon the characteristics of the generating plant.

The present problems with electric vehicles arise primarily from the low storage capacities of the available batteries and the large weight and size of the batteries and motors. However, research and development is proceeding in some countries. In the Federal Republic of Germany, for example, BMW have recently (Ward's Engine Update, 1989b) modified eight of their 325ix cars with an electrical system making use of high energy sodium-sulphur (Na/S) batteries. These are claimed to have many advantages over lead batteries and the car, with a 2-speed automatic transmission, has a top speed of 62mph (100km/h) and a range of 93 miles (150 km) in city driving. Acceleration from zero to 31mph (50km/h) takes 9 seconds. One problem is that heating needs to be provided by a small separate hot-water heater, at present burning diesel fuel.

In recent years some attention has been given to the use of fuel cells instead of batteries in electric vehicles (Design Engineering, 1989). Most of the vehicles built in this way have so far been hybrids, utilising a combination of batteries to provide peak power, with fuel cells to provide cruising power, plus what is needed to recharge the batteries. This has resulted in weight penalties and poor performance. However the Commission of the European Communities (CEC) has recently initiated work on direct methanol fuel cells as part of the non-nuclear energy research and development programme.

Development in the USA. Whilst most major European manufacturing countries have tended to rely on their vehicle industries in deciding standards, the USA has employed a totally opposite approach for development in this field in that, under the leadership of the Environment Protection Agency (EPA), standards have been set for emissions and other relevant levels which industry is then expected to meet. For example, in the knowledge that the emission of carbon dioxide is more or less proportional to the amount of fuel used, and other emissions also increase in roughly this way, the "Corporate Average Fuel Economy" (CAFE) requirement is likely to become more severe in the future. This US Government regulation requires that the average fuel consumption across the range of models sold by each manufacturer shall not exceed a specified amount. The policy was first introduced in response to the fuel shortages of the 1970's, and it has been very successful over the years in producing a continuing and very substantial improvement in average miles per gallon. Currently (Treuthart, 1989) the CAFE value stands at 26.5mpg, but in the light of concern over greenhouse gases the EPA have recently proposed a 40 mpg standard by the year 2,000 and 75mpg by 2,025. The State of California is seriously considering a compulsory move towards alternative fuels, and, early in the next century, the banning of petrol engines. State funding for appropriate development programmes is being provided by the South Coast Air Quality Management District (Osenga, 1988) of $5.9 million annually to 1990, and $6.2 million annually after that until, at the moment, 1993.

To try to meet these pressures, all USA domestic vehicle manufacturers have built cars (Flax, 1989) that can run on methanol, ethanol, petrol, or some combination of the three. There are also many development programmes for electric vehicles, and gas turbine engines.

Diesel engine emissions are also being treated in the same way (Karylko, 1988). The EPA requires, for example, that all new engines installed in urban buses must meet by 1991 particulate emission levels that are 83 per cent lower than today's standards. It is widely thought that, even equipped with traps or low-sulphur fuel, diesel engines will not meet these requirements, and methanol or compressed natural gas are looked upon as possible solutions. The US Government has already made $50 million available for the purchase of buses running on alternative fuels. Such development could also be applied to heavy-duty lorries to meet tighter standards for their particulate emissions that are due to come into effect in 1994.

5.4 Chapter 5 References

ARAI M, S MUJASHITA and K SATO, (1987) Development and selection of diesel regeneration schemes. SAE Paper 870012, SAE Warrendale.

BARRY, E G, L J McGABE, D H GERKE and J M PEREZ, (1985) Heavy duty diesel engine fuels combusion performance and emissions - a co-operative research programme. SAE Paper 852078, SAE, Warrendale.

BIRCH S, (1988) Hydrogen-powered vehicles. Automotive Engienering, December.

COLWILL, D M (editor), (1974) The assessment of a lead trap for motor vehicles. TRRL Report LR 662. Transport and Road Research Laboratory, Crowthorne.

COMMISSION OF THE EUROPEAN COMMUNITIES, (1983) Report of the ad-hoc Group ERGA - Air Pollution. Report III/602.83 - EN-Final. EC Commission. Brussels.

COMPRESSED AIR MAGAZINE, (1989) Aiming at the hydrogen economy.

CONCAWE, (1987) Volatile organic compound emissions in Western Europe - Control options and cost effectiveness for gasoline vehicles, distribution and refining. Report·No 6/87, CONCAWE, The Hague.

DESIGN ENGINEERING, (1989) Fuel cells - the search for improved performance. July.

ENVIRONMENTAL PROTECTION AGENCY (AUSTRALIA), (undated) A guide to unleaded petrol catalyst strategy. Aust. EPA, Melbourne.

ENVIRONMENTAL PROTECTION AGENCY (USA), (1986) Standards for emissions from methanol fuelled motor vehicles and motor vehicle engines. Report AMS-FRL-2974-50, EPA, Ann Arbor.

EVANS W D J and A J J WILKINS, (1985) Single bed three way catalyst in the European environment. SAE Paper 852096, SAE, Warrendale.

FELGER G, (1987) Engine management systems - a substantial contribution to emission control. Proceedings of a conference "Vehicle emissions and their impact on European air quality" I.Mech. E. London.

FLAX A, (1989) No easy answer to new fuels, high CAFE, low emissions. Automotive News, May.

FREEMAN, H D, (1989) Heavy duty diesel emission control - implications for fuel consumption. Atmospheric ozone research and its policy implications. Elsevier Science Publishers. B.V. Amasterdam.

HARDENBURG H O, (1987) Urban bus application of a ceramic fibre coil particulate trap. SAE Paper 870016 SAE Warrendale.

HICKMAN, A J and C JAFFRAY, (1986) Performance and durability of a catalyst trap oxidiser installed on a city bus for 65,000 miles of revenue service. SAE paper 860138.

HICKMAN, A J and C G B MITCHELL, (1989) Technical and economic implications of regulations on air pollution and noise from road vehicles. OECD/ECMJ Special Ministerial Conference on Transport and the Environment, Background Paper.

HODGSON, M A, (1987) The Ford central fuel injection system. Proceedings of a Conference "Vehicle emissions and their impact on European air quality" I.Mech. E., London.

HOLLIS, T, (1984) Literature study of the feasibility and possible impact of reduced emission levels from diesel engined vehicles. Report No DP 84/812, Ricardo Consulting Engineers, Shoreham-by-Sea.

INGHAM M C and R B WARDEN, (1987) Cost effectiveness of diesel fuel modifications for particulate control. SAE Paper 870556 Warrendale.

INSTITUTE OF PETROLEUM, (1986) A review of diesel quality world-wide, Petroleum Review, London.

KOBAYASHI N, T AKATSUKA, J NAKANO, T KAMO and S MATSUHITA, (1984) Development of the Toyota lean combusion system. JSAE Review, pp 106-112.

KARYLKO D, (1988) Tough diesel rules spur research for cleaner bus engine. Automotive News, November.

LATHAM, S and P R TONKIN, (1988) TRRL Report RR158, Transport and Road Research Laboratory, Crowthorne.

LAWSON A, H C VERGEER, W DRUMMOND, J P MORGAN and E D DAINTY, (1985) Performance of a ceramic diesel particulate trap over typical mining duty cycles using fuel additives. SAE paper 850150, Society of Automotive Engineers, Warrendale.

NATIONAL ENGINEERING LABORATORY, (1983) The influence of oxygenates on spark ignition engine performance - a review of literature. Report No TRAN/01, National Engineering Laboratory, East Kilbride.

OSENGA M, (1988) California clean fuels program. Diesel Progress North American, April.

PEARCE, T C and G P DAVIES (1990). In service exhaust emissions from advanced technology cars. TRRL Research Report in publication. Transport and Road Research Laboratory, Crowthorne.

RAO V D, J E WHITE, W R WADE, M G AIMONE and H A CIKANEK, (1985) Advanced techniques for thermal and catalytic diesel particulate trap regeneration. SAE paper 850014, Society of Automotive engineers, Warrendale.

RIJKEBOER R C, J A N van LING and J van der WEIDE, (1986) The catalytic trap oxidizer on a city bus: a Dutch demonstration program. SAE paper 860134, Society of Automotive Engineers, Warrendale.

SMALL K A, (1988) Reducing transit bus emissions: comparative costs and benefits of methanol, particulate traps and fuel modification. Transportation Research Record, No 1164, 15-22, Washington.

TONKIN, P R and P ETHERIDGE, (1987) A new study of the feasibility and possible impact of reduced emission levels from diesel engined vehicles. Report No DP 97/0927, Ricardo Consulting Engineers. Shoreham-by-Sea. 1987.

TRANSPORT ENGINEER, (1987) London, January.

TREUTHART P, (1989) Fast cars threatened by new regulations. Autocar and Motor, May.

WARD'S ENGINE UPDATE, (1989a) BMW explores electrically powered cars. June.

WARD'S ENGINE UPDATE, (1989b) While BMW delves into hydrogen fuel. June.

WEAVER C S, C MILLER, W A JOHNSON and T S HIGGINS, (1986) Reducing the sulfur and aromatic content of diesel fuels - costs, benefits and effectiveness for emissions control. SAE paper 860622, Society of Automotive Engineers, Warrendale.

6 Surveys and Forecasting

This Chapter looks at field surveys that have been made, both of the pollutants themselves and of subjective response to them, and at methods of forecasting the pollution levels that will occur in different traffic and road conditions.

6.1 Field Surveys of pollution

6.1.1 Lead in the atmosphere

Unleaded petrol is rapidly coming into general use, but in the run-up to this situation many surveys were made specifically of the concentration of atmospheric lead due to exhaust emissions, and it will be useful to give a brief account of some of them here.

A valuable long-term study of lead emission has been carried out by the Transport and Road Research Laboratory on the M4 motorway, at a site near Harlington, Middlesex (Hickman, 1989). The site location is shown in Figure 6.1, and was chosen because it was in the centre of one of the busiest motorways in the UK. The influence of non-traffic sources of pollution was minimal and, because of the high flow of traffic, pollution levels were high. Changes in pollution could be clearly observed as Figure 6.2 shows and, except for random variations due to varying weather conditions, were caused entirely by changes in vehicle emissions. Broadly, the airborne lead content followed the changes in the average lead content of petrol. During the period from 1981 to 1984, the average lead content of petrol was relatively stable at 0.37-0.38 g/l and from 1986 to 1987 it was stable at 0.14 g/l, the reduction between these periods being about 63 per cent. The resulting reduction in atmospheric lead concentration was from 9.0 to 2.8 mg/m^3, a reduction of 69 per cent.

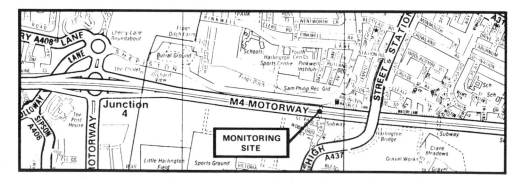

Fig 6.1   Site location

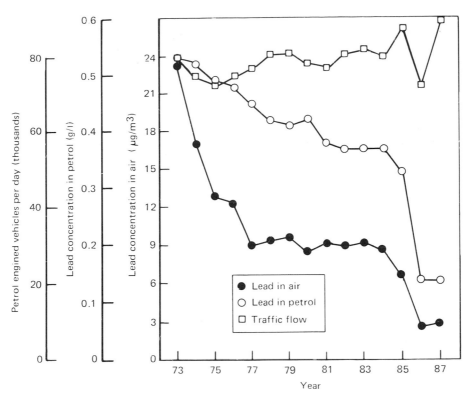

Fig 6.2   Average lead in air, lead in petrol and flow of petrol engined vehicles

This study covered a very interesting period in 1973/4 (Hogbin and Bevan, 1976) when, owing to a crisis in the supply of fuel, a speed limit of 80 km/h (50 mph) was imposed in December 1973, and lasted about 4 months. Figure 6.3 shows the variation in weekly lead concentration over a length of time including this 4 month period, together with average speeds at the site. The maximum lead content of fuel fell appreciably at this time, but average content fell by very little, and there is no doubt at all that the sharp drop in lead emission at the end of 1973 was almost entirely due to the drop in average vehicle speeds. The figure also shows how the emission rates increased again as speeds increased after the 80 km/h limit was removed, although to a slightly lower level than previously.

Measurements of ambient airborne particulate lead concentrations were also made in Central London from 1973 to 1979 by the Warren Spring Laboratory (Dorling and Sullivan, 1980). During this period there was a decrease in average particulate lead levels of between one and two per cent per year, attributed entirely to the decrease in the average lead content of petrol during the same period.

Another study was made in 1973 (Colwill and Hickman, 1973), this time of some specific situations where lead levels might be expected to be unusually high, including two filling stations and an urban road tunnel. One petrol filling station (A) was situated alongside a principal road in a small market town, and used a self-service system which tends to increase spillage. The other (B) was alongside a principal road in a large town,

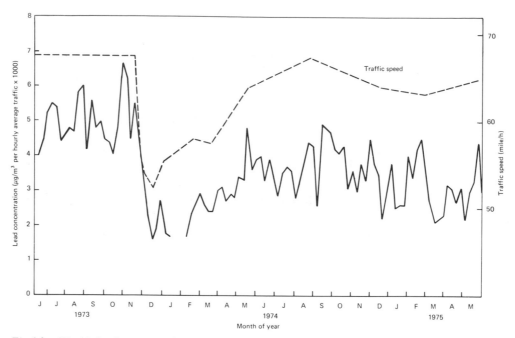

Fig 6.3   Weekly lead concentration in air (adjusted for traffic flow)

also used a self-service system, was open continuously, and sold a much greater volume of fuel than the first one. The heavily-trafficked tunnel is in central London, and has a ventilation system. Measurements were confined to lead but unusually, not only was particulate lead measured but so also was volatile lead, in order to determine the true total lead content of the air. Volatile lead comes primarily from the evaporation of fuel, and is thus likely to be insignificant in a normal road situation. It was, however, thought that it could be significant in a filling station.

The results of the monitoring are given in Table 6.1. The concentrations of the particulate lead, the volatile lead components and the total lead are recorded together with the proportion the volatile lead compounds form of the total lead pollution. Since a continuous method of sampling was used in this work the data given in Table 6.1 represent an average atmospheric concentration for the period of collection.

At filling station A the total lead level in the atmosphere varied during the four sampling periods but the volatile lead compounds formed a remarkably consistent proportion of the total of approximately 55 per cent. The variations in the total lead in the various sampling periods can be attributed to differences in vehicle movements and fuel sales during the periods. It was noted during this work that there were spillages of fuel by people operating the self-service pumps; the position of the spillages relative to the sampling point may account for some of the variation in the data. The consistency of the results suggests that the local topography, particularly the canopy over the pumps, regulated the air movements around the pumps, markedly reducing the effects of the variations in wind speed and direction.

TABLE 6.1

Results of measurements of lead concentrations at three sites (1973)

Site	Collection period	Volatile lead (g/m^3)	Particulate lead (g/m^3)	Total lead (g/m^3)	Volatile lead as percentage of total
Filling Station A	20 June-30 June	0.92	0.63	1.59	59.4
	30 June-11 July	1.11	0.89	2.00	55.5
	11 July-21 July	1.54	1.20	2.74	56.2
	21 July-25 July	1.33	1.40	2.73	48.7
Filling Station B	20 July-24 July	0.64	1.06	1.70	37.6
	31 July-4 August	0.48	1.07	1.55	31.0
	11 August-18 August	0.46	1.17	1.63	28.2
	18 August-25 August	0.49	1.17	1.66	29.6
	25 August-30 August	1.03	0.83	1.86	55.4[a]
Underground tunnel	10 August-15 August	1.24	3.32	4.56	27.2
	15 August-24 August	1.72	25.84	27.52	6.3
	21 Sept.-28 Sept.	0.75	8.63	9.38	8.0
	28 Sept.-3 October	1.24	12.90	14.14	8.8

[a] Fuel spillage observed.

A similar situation was found at filling station B, but the total lead pollution was lower than at filling station A and the volatile lead compounds formed a consistent, but smaller, proportion of the total. The exceptionally high value for the volatile lead compounds obtained during 25-30 August is attributed to an observed spillage of fuel during the filling of the storage tanks. It was noted that fuel spillage also occurred at this site during the operation of the self-service pumps. The consistency in the values obtained may again be attributed to the local topography and to the canopy over the pumps reducing the dispersive effect of changes in wind speed and direction. Although there were more vehicle movements and greater sales at filling station B, the total lead pollution was generally considerably less than that found at filling station A; this difference may be attributed to local topography, filling station B being in a more exposed position.

There was much greater variation in the lead levels found in the tunnel than in those found in the filling stations. Although there was considerable variation in the total lead pollution the proportion contributed by volatile lead compounds was reasonably consistent except during the period 10-15 August. In this period there was a marked reduction in the traffic using the tunnel because of industrial disputes in the docks. Although wide variations have been found in the total lead pollution in the tunnel, traffic data are not available to relate directly pollution and vehicle movements. It seems unlikely, however, that the traffic pattern in the tunnel changed during the monitoring period by the factor of three shown by some of the pollution measurements, so there must be an unknown factor exercising considerable influence on pollutant levels. The volatile lead compounds appear normally to contribute approximately 8 per cent of the total lead pollution in this particular tunnel. The general public do not remain in such situations long enough to absorb appreciable quantities of lead; the same, however, may not be true of people such as forecourt staff.

6.1.2   Other pollutants

At about the same time that these lead measurements were being made, the Transport and Road Research Laboratory was also measuring the concentration of other exhaust emission pollutants in the atmosphere in Reading (Colwill, 1976), Coventry (Hickman *et al.*, 1976), and London (Hickman, 1976).

Measurements were first made in the town of Reading, at two sites, one on a heavily trafficked road and one control site in an area remote from traffic. Next, four sites were investigated in Coventry, chosen to include a range of residential, industrial and commercial situations. Shortly afterwards measurements were made in West London at sites particularly chosen to examine the change in pollutant levels with increasing distance from a heavily trafficked road. Table 6.2 gives the results of these measurements. It should be noted that the sites differed; the types of traffic differed; and, importantly, wind speeds and other meteorological factors differed. One would not, therefore, expect there to be any simple correlation in such a Table between pollutant levels and traffic flow. The actual levels are, however, interesting as compared with various air quality standards recommended at the time and these are shown in Table 6.3, taking the London values as reasonably representative. The remarkably high one hour concentration of nitrogen dioxide should be noted.

In 1979, a study was made (Colwill and Hickman, 1979) to investigate possible road safety consequences of drivers breathing polluted air. For the measurements, 11 new cars were driven around a 35 km route comprising heavily trafficked roads in and around London, and the concentrations of carbon monoxide inside and immediately outside the vehicles were continuously monitored. Average levels of carbon monoxide between 12 and 60 ppm were found inside the cars, and these levels were between 30 and 80 per cent of the external concentrations. The internal levels varied according to external changes but the changes were greatly damped by the buffering effect of the ventilation system. Differences in internal carbon monoxide levels were more marked between vehicles than for different runs in the same vehicle and were probably due to differences in the ventilation systems.

Blood carboxy-haemoglobin concentrations which would arise from the carbon monoxide exposures were calculated. Published data suggest that carboxy-haemoglobin concentrations within the range found (1.5-3.0 per cent) would not be expected to produce an adverse effect on health (see Section 4.11); there are conflicting views as to whether driving performance would be impaired. It is possible that any impairment

TABLE 6.2

Pollutant Levels Measured at Sites in England

Pollutant	London North Circular Road May-June 1979	London North Circular Road Weekdays	Coventry (Nov-Dec. 1973) Residential	Coventry (Nov-Dec. 1973) Shopping	Coventry (Nov-Dec. 1973) Mixed	Reading (Dec. 1971) Residential	Reading (Dec. 1971) Main Road
Carbon monoxide (ppm)	4	6	10	3	2	2	6
	(0, 18)	(0, 7)	(0, 35)	(0, 27)	(0, 8)	(0, 6)	(2, 10)
Total hydrocarbons (ppm)	4	4	7	5	4	3	5
	(2, 8)	(2, 6)	(3, 17)	(3, 9)	(2, 7)	(2, 6)	(2, 9)
Methane (ppm)	1.6	1.5	2.1	1.8	1.8	1.3	Not measured
	(1.1, 3.7)	(1.0, 6.0)	(1.0, 4.0)	(0, 4.0)	(1.3, 3.6)	(1.2, 2.2)	
Ethylene (pphm)	7	8	5	3	2	1	Not measured
	(1, 21)	(4, 6)	(0, 20)	(0, 17)	(0, 8)	(0, 7)	
Acetylene (pphm)	7	8	6	4	3	1	Not measured
	(0, 28)	(3, 9)	(0, 27)	(0, 25)	(0, 20)	(0, 8)	
NO_x (pphm)	27	32	25	21	20	14	Not measured
	(2, 113)	(1, 2)	(5, 59)	(2, 80)	(2, 60)	(1, 68)	
Particulate lead (g/m³)	1.4	1.8	3.0	1.8	1.7	1.5	0.9
	(0.1, 5.5)	(0, 6.0)	(0.9, 7.2)	(1.2, 2.5)	n/a	(1.0, 2.1)	(0, 1.0)
Traffic (vehicles/h)	3500	5300	1200	830	830	670	1200

Figures in brackets represent minimum and maximum hourly average values, except for lead where they give minima and maxima for the actual sampling periods (3 to 5 h London, whole day Coventry, 6 h Reading). The bracketed figure for carbon monoxide, London weekdays is the average overnight level and is therefore relatively low.

TABLE 6.3

London (North Circular Road) Pollutant Maximum Levels Compared with Various Recommended Standards

Pollutant	Averaging period	Measured level	WHO Report 506 (1972)	WHO Report 4 (1977)	US National Air Quality Standards (1970)
Carbon	1 h	17.7 ppm	35 ppm[a]	-	35 ppm[a]
monoxide	8 h	9.6 ppm	9 ppm[a]	-	9 ppm[a]
Nitrogen	1 h	62 pphm[c]	-	17 pphm[b]	-
dioxide	Survey period	5 pphm[d]	-	-	-
	Annual	-	-	-	5 pphm (primary)

[a] Not to be exceeded more than once per year.
[b] Not to be exceeded more than once per month.
[c] Estimated as 55 per cent of NO_x (113)
[d] Estimated as 20 per cent of NO_x (27).

might be significant if the driver were confronted with a dangerous situation which demanded quick reaction. Ramsey (1970) showed a significant increase in the reaction times of drivers and passengers exposed to an average of 38.1 ppm of carbon monoxide for 90 min, and significant effects on the ability of subjects to perceive differences in the duration of auditory stimuli have been observed for concentrations of less than 50 ppm (Bear and Wertheim, 1967). However, Hosko (1970) found no effects on reaction time, manual dexterity or the ability to estimate the passage of time for concentrations of 100 ppm or less. Most other investigators have studied the effects of considerably higher carboxy-haemoglobin levels. Wright et al (1973) for example, using a driving simulation test, showed a significant deterioration in careful driving habits resulting from carboxy-haemoglobin levels of 6-7 per cent. McFarland (1973), however, concluded that a 6 per cent carboxy-haemoglobin level has no effect on the driving ability and that 11 and 17 per cent levels had no serious effect. Ury et al (1972) compared motor accident and pollution statistics and found no correlation between carbon monoxide levels and accidents. Overall, then, no conclusions can yet be drawn as to whether the levels found in the TRRL study (Colwill and Hickman, 1979) are likely to impair driving performance significantly.

A typical urban enclosed car park was examined in 1975 (Bevan and Hickman, 1975). Few vehicles entered before 0800h, then the traffic intake remained fairly constant until 1700h when it fell to the very low overnight flow. The car park consists of three storeys, each approximately rectangular, over a shopping precinct. The first and second storeys are closed on three sides with the fourth side open from about 1m to ceiling level (about 2m). A ventilation system is provided for these two levels; the third storey is completely open. Measurements were made in the part of the park judged most likely to suffer the greatest pollution because of the layout and because of the traffic movement, and Figure 6.4 shows the diurnal variation of five pollutants. The concentrations were quite a lot higher than those to which people are normally exposed at the roadside, and although they are unlikely to be harmful to the normal user, who is exposed for only a short time, they could cause harm (particularly from carbon monoxide) to anyone exposed for a long period.

As part of the development of a prediction procedure for air pollution, described later, pollution levels were measured (Brennan and McCrae, 1988) near a motorway in a cutting in 1988. Summaries of the pollutant levels recorded at the mobile laboratory are given in Table 6.4 and Figure 6.5.

In general, the levels of the various pollutants corresponded with those expected at a roadside location of this type, and were well below generally recommended maximum levels for exposure. In comparison with those at urban sites the levels of carbon monoxide and hydrocarbons were lower and the levels of oxides of nitrogen higher. It is likely that this was because of the emission characteristics of the traffic on the motorway. The rates of emission of carbon monoxide and hydrocarbons are strongly influenced by the speed of the vehicle (see Section 2.5), with the highest rates at low speed. Thus the freely flowing, high speed motorway traffic would give rise to lower levels than congested urban flows. Oxides of nitrogen emissions are highest at high speed, again corresponding with the relatively high observed airborne concentrations at this site.

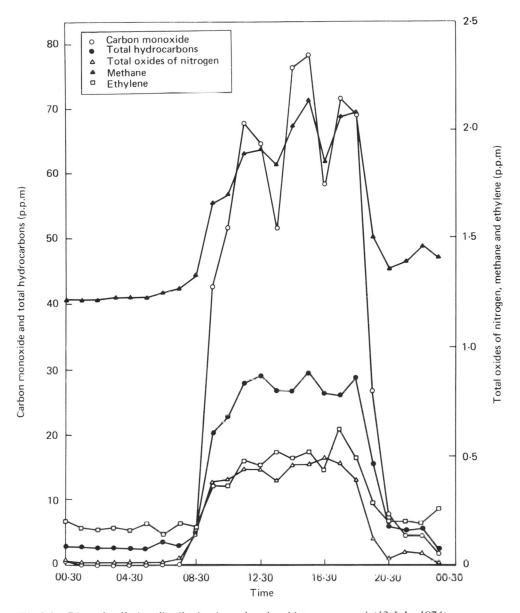

Fig 6.4   Diurnal pollution distribution in enclosed multistorey car park (12 July, 1974)

It would be expected that the levels of carbon monoxide and oxides of nitrogen would vary in accordance with the volume of traffic on the motorway and, in general, this was so, with significantly higher concentrations during the day than overnight. However, as shown in Figure 6.5, a slight reduction in nitric oxide concentrations was noted between 0800 and 0900 hours during the weekdays (when the traffic volume was highest), in combination with a high carbon monoxide concentration. After the peak traffic hour there was a disproportionate reduction in carbon monoxide concentration compared with the reduction in traffic flow and an increase, for several hours, in the nitric oxide concentration. This section of the M25 carries very high traffic flows during the morning

TABLE 6.4

Atmospheric pollution levels on the M25 Motorway near junction 11

Pollutant	average 24 hour concentration		average 1 hour concentration (0800 - 0900 Mon to Fri)
	Total week (Mon-Sun)	Weekday (Mon-Fri)	
Carbon monoxide (ppm)	2.33	2.39	5.9
Nitric oxide (ppb)	605.4	624.1	1256.0
Nitrogen dioxide (ppb)	20.2	21.3	76.0
Total oxides of nitrogen (ppb)	620.5	636.0	1239.0
Ozone (ppb)	5.3	5.5	10.0
Sulphur dioxide (ppb)	32.2	31.8	44.0
Total hydrocarbons (ppm)	2.31	2.36	5.2
Methane (ppm)	1.97	1.99	3.5
Non methane hydrocarbons (ppm)	0.54	0.56	3.5
Total suspended particulates (g/m^3)	58.7	-	-
Particulate lead (g/m^3)	1.18	-	-

peak period, so traffic becomes congested and vehicles move more slowly, resulting in variations in pollutant emission rates. However, in spite of the variability of the traffic speeds, significant correlations were found between traffic volume and the vehicle derived pollutants carbon monoxide, oxides of nitrogen, lead and non-methane hydrocarbons.

The average airborne lead concentration of 1.2 $\mu g/m^3$ was much lower than levels recorded at motorway sites in the past as a result of the reduction in the maximum permitted lead content of petrol from 0.4 g/l to 0.15 g/l in January 1986.

For about one year from 1984 to 1985 the Borough of Southwark in London in co-operation with the Greater London Council carried out a very thorough programme of measurement (London Borough of Southwark, 1985) at 14 sites across the borough, ranging from the immediate sides of busy roads to upper storeys and roofs. They then compared their results with current appropriate EC, WHO or US air quality standards. The results showed, as one might expect, high levels of atmospheric pollution. Their measurements of NO_2 were admitted to be inadequate as far as instrumentation was concerned, but it was evident that the EC guidelines were unlikely to be met; and CO guidelines (WHO, US Federal AQS - 9ppm as an 8 hour mean and 35 ppm as an hourly mean once per year) were exceeded on occasions at all the roadside sites, and particularly at one site on the Old Kent Road where during certain periods the guide value was

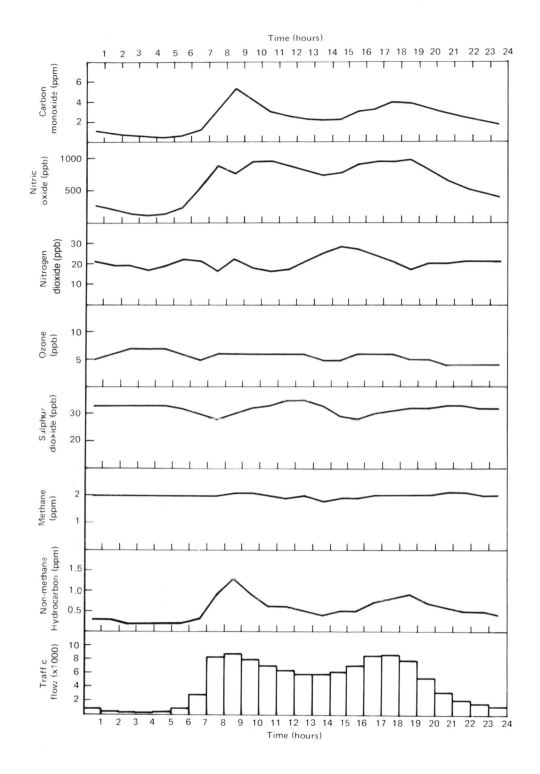

Fig 6.5   Average hourly variation of pollutants and traffic on weekdays, motorway in cutting

137

exceeded more often than it was complied with. The deposition of particulates was also found to be a considerable problem resulting in discomfort, and soiling of clothes and buildings.

This last problem has been studied elsewhere, as for example in Marseille, France (Joumard *et al.*, 1983), where it was concluded that the same number of diesel engines would emit some four to five times the quantity of troublesome particulates as would be emitted by petrol engines.

Roadside surveys of this type measure levels of pollution to which people may be exposed, but they do not account for variations in exposure that result from an individual's changes in location and activity and so do not give an accurate representation of personal exposures. Hickman (1989) measured the personal exposures of a small group of subjects using miniature analyers carried by them during their normal activities. For the non-smokers in the sample, about 25 per cent of their intake of CO was traffic related. The remainder was from prolonged exposure to lower levels indoors.

6.2 Subjective response

The assessment of subjective response to environmental problems is always a very difficult and complex task, and attitudes to air pollution present one of the most difficult. The problems involved have been discussed under the heading 'subjective effects' in Chapter 4, and the results of a large scale survey on "road traffic and the environment", in so far as they relate to air pollution, have been mentioned in that Chapter.

In January 1989 another report (Ashdown Environmental Limited, 1989) was produced for TRRL that drew on the earlier survey and on other sources, and confirmed earlier views that the vehicle exhaust pollutants of most direct concern to people are smoke and odour, putting the blame for most of this on diesel emissions from heavy lorries. Exhaust emissions and traffic noise are roughly equivalent in terms of perceived nuisance.

More recent opinion polls seem to suggest that there is an increasing concern with vehicle exhaust emissions in a more general environmental fashion, largely because of recent publicity given to problems such as acid rain and the greenhouse effect. It is not yet clear, however, whether or not the general public is beginning to realise the possible ultimate impact of these problems on, for example, private car ownership.

It is often suggested that monetary values should be sought across the whole field of environmental nuisance, so that the "polluter pays" principle can be employed, and also so that an economic component can be incorporated into the general cost-benefit approach used to assess highway projects, no less in air pollution than in noise, visual intrusion and other factors. The studies so far carried out in this area have led to very little of use, and there are very great difficulties in assigning monetary eqivalents to environmental disturbance. People are generally unwilling or unable to ascribe a value to a particular environmental factor, especially where they themselves may bear the burden of financial responsibility, through increased vehicle restrictions or dearer house prices. It is not even easy to state who is the principal polluter - the car owner? the manufacturer? the oil company? the highway authority? and so on. The general consensus has been that such economic assessments are not viable and that efforts to quantify the subjective effects of vehicle pollutants should be directed elsewhere, though the monetary approach is currently being reinvestigated in full appreciation of the inevitable limitation of any such costing methodology.

6.3 Estimating air pollution from road traffic data

In the UK, the Advisory Committee on Trunk Road Assessment recommended (Report of the Advisory Committee on Trunk Road Assessment, 1977) that "a special air quality report should be prepared when air pollution is likely to be a problem" - otherwise it should be omitted from the assessment of proposed schemes for new roads or road improvements. However this rather begged the question since it is not easy to see how it can be known whether or not it is likely to be a problem without doing some form of prediction, and in any case experience suggests that the public do perceive air pollution as a problem with most road schemes, particularly when roads are planned in and around heavily populated urban areas. Accordingly the Transport and Road Research Laboratory has developed two procedures for making such an assessment, the first being a computer-based method that is as accurate as it can be bearing in mind the inherent innaccuracies in the whole subject, and the second being a simple graphical, and more approximate, method to be used to indicate whether air pollution from traffic around a particular road system requires more detailed study. There follows a brief summary of the procedures; for full instructions for use the references must be consulted.

6.3.1 Computer method (Hickman and Colwill, 1982)

Gaussian dispersion was assumed as the starting point of the model. In order that complex road layouts might be considered, the roads have been regarded as linear sets of point sources and not as lines. This, while considerably increasing the computation required, makes it possible to apply the method to urban road networks as well as rural, isolated roads. The roads are also subdivided into sections according to their type and position so that the characteristics of the traffic might be separately specified for each section. This permits a more detailed consideration of exhaust emission rates which are significantly related to the vehicle operating conditions.

Varying wind speeds and wind directions are also considered by this method. Winds oblique to roads lead to higher concentrations nearby than perpendicular winds and, in a network of roads, the wind does not blow at the same angle to them all. Therefore, it has been made possible to specify any wind direction whose choice may be governed by particular requirements, for example, 'worst case' situations where the wind blows towards a populated area or parallel with the most heavily trafficked road. The speed of the wind may be chosen as it also has a significant effect on pollutant levels. Generally, the higher the wind speed, the lower the pollutant levels, so it is often desirable to make estimates for low wind speeds to represent the worst likely conditions for dispersion. It may be known, however, that a site is very exposed to high winds or unusually well sheltered, in which cases appropriate wind speed values may be chosen.

A simplified schematic of the model is shown in Figure 6.6.

The model has been developed to predict carbon monoxide concentrations. Carbon monoxide was chosen because it is possible to measure atmospheric concentrations continuously and thus provide data for testing the model over short periods when there are considerable fluctuations in traffic flows and meteorological conditions. The carbon monoxide concentrations estimated by the model will give a good indication of where air pollution by other exhaust components is likely to be a problem, and where there will be significant changes in pollutant levels.

The emission rates depend on the volume of traffic using a road, its composition and the operating mode of the vehicles. Two assumptions have been made which greatly simplify the calculation and input requirement. Firstly it has been assumed that petrol- and diesel-engine vehicles emit equal amounts of carbon monoxide. This is justified in that the lower concentration of carbon monoxide in diesel exhaust is offset by the larger total volume of exhaust produced by large diesel engines. By making this assumption, the dependency of emission rates on traffic composition is eliminated and only total

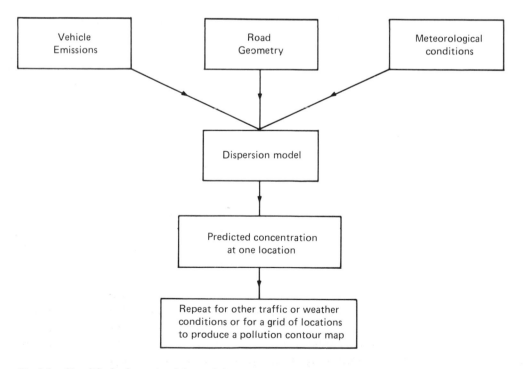

Fig 6.6   Simplified schematic of the model

140

traffic flows need be known. Secondly, a single factor, vehicle speed, was chosen to represent the engine operating mode. Thus the following simple expression is used to calculate the source emission rates Q:

$$Q = 1.031 \, TS^{-0.795} \times 10^{-4} g/m.s$$

where   T = total traffic flow (veh/h)
         S = mean traffic speed (km/h)

This quantity is multiplied by the number of metres separating the point sources along a road section to give the emission rate of a point representing that length of road.

The expression was determined from the analysis of data on in-service emissions of British vehicles and data from the USA on the relationship between carbon monoxide emissions and mean vehicle speed.

Periods of idling, acceleration and deceleration, gear changes and similar manoeuvres all produce associated changes in emission rate and, as additional data on vehicle emissions and more detailed information concerning their behaviour become available, it may be possible to improve this evaluation substantially by consideration of such factors.

Hickman and Colwill (1982) give details of the manner in which wind speed and direction and other factors affecting the dispersal of the pollutants are taken into account in the model, and need not be repeated here. Working on these factors, traffic information, and road layout as basic inputs, the computer programme provides information about the dispersal of carbon monoxide in numerical and map form.

To illustrate the range of accuracy typical of results obtained by this method, carbon monoxide concentrations have been estimated from observed traffic and meteorological data from three roadside locations. These are compared with the measured carbon monoxide levels in Figures 6.7, 6.8 and 6.9.

The first site was near a single, heavily trafficked road in a rural area; the second was near a very busy, traffic-light controlled intersection in an urban area and the third was near to the portal of a busy road tunnel. Thus, a wide range of situations, resulting in a wide range of carbon monoxide concentrations, is represented.

In order to give a measure of the accuracy of the estimates, the data have been grouped according to the difference between the estimated and measured levels and the results of this analysis are shown in Figure 6.10. Figure 6.10A shows the range of deviations in absolute terms and, as might be expected, the size of the ranges at the different sites vary in the same way as the ranges of concentration. Thus, at the rural site, where the maximum observed value was about 9 ppm, most estimates (97 per cent) are within ±2.5 ppm of the observed concentration. At the urban site, where levels up to about 15 ppm were measured, 91 per cent of the estimates are within ±4 ppm of the observed concentration and at the tunnel site, where the highest level was about 30 ppm, 88 per cent of the estimates are within ±8 ppm of the observed levels.

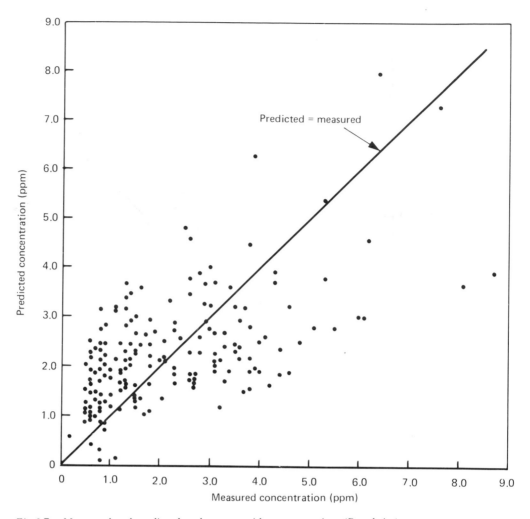

Fig 6.7   Measured and predicted carbon monoxide concentrations (Rural site)

In Figure 6.10B, the deviations are shown as percentages of the observed values. By this method, the data for the tunnel site show the closest agreement. Here, 86 per cent of the estimates are within ±50 per cent of the measured values. At the urban site 74 per cent and at the rural site 57 per cent of the estimates are within that range.

Although there is a good general correspondence between estimated and observed levels, it is also clear that individual estimates may vary considerably from the actual concentrations. For this reason, no estimated concentration should be regarded as a numerically accurate prediction but as a general indication of the level likely to be experienced, and, for the same reason, it is good practice, wherever possible, to calculate concentrations for the existing situation as well as for the proposed scheme and to consider the changes that would result from the construction rather than the absolute predicted levels.

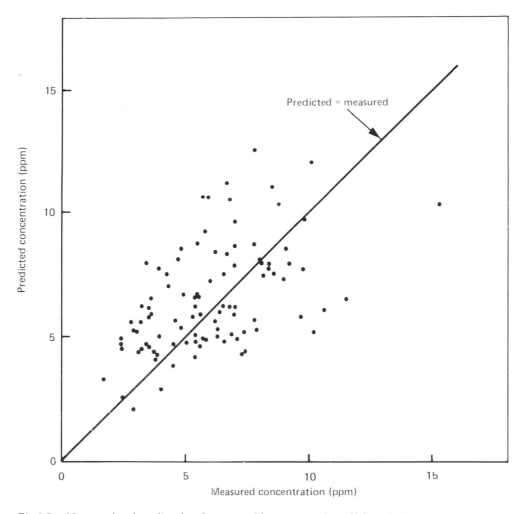

Fig 6.8   Measured and predicted carbon monoxide concentrations (Urban site)

More recent studies have attempted to improve some aspects of the model. The method of calculating emission rates was re-examined as more data became available from a number of studies carried out for TRRL (Colwill *et al*, 1984). In spite of several reductions in emission limits, no significant change in emission characteristics of UK vehicles in service was found, and the original emission rate calculation was retained. A series of pollution and traffic surveys has been carried out at locations where the site topography would be expected to exert a strong influence on the dispersion of the pollutants (eg urban street 'canyons' or elevated roadways) (McCrae and Hickman, 1989). The results of these studies will be incorporated in a revised model capable of more accurate forecasts for this type of site.

143

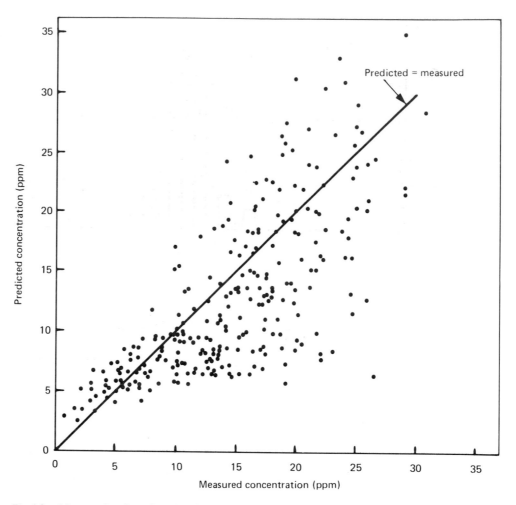

Fig 6.9   Measured and predicted carbon monoxide concentrations (Tunnel site)

6.3.2   Presentation and interpretation of computer model results

The required presentation of pollutant levels predicted by the model may vary at different locations. Where there is a particularly sensitive area, such as housing or a public building very near to a proposed road development, it may be desirable to study the likely impact of the traffic at that site under a range of conditions. Other proposed routes, particularly in urban districts, may be so located that their impact on the whole of the surrounding area is important. It has been made possible, therefore, to suit the model output to a variety of circumstances. Four methods are available, which are:

1.   Prediction at a single receptor for varying meteorological conditions.

2.   Prediction at a single receptor for varying traffic flows.

144

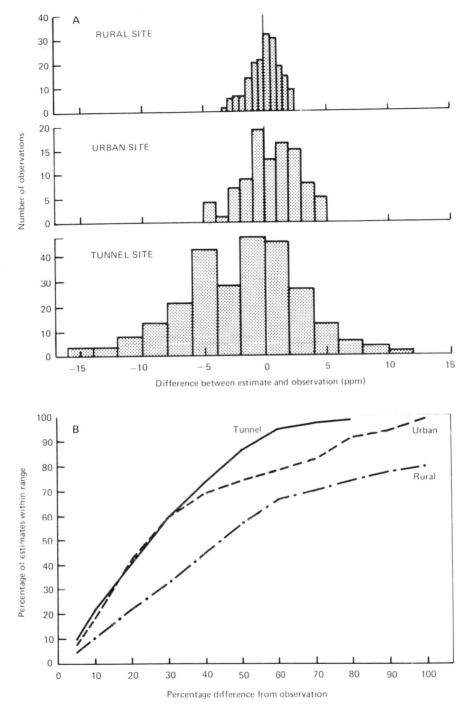

Fig 6.10 Accuracy of the prediction from the TRRL air pollution model

145

3. Prediction at a single receptor for varying meteorological conditions and traffic flows.

4. Predictions at a grid of receptors for one set of meteorological conditions and traffic flows.

For the first three methods the results are given numerically. This is also true for method 4 but, additionally, the results are produced in the form of input to a computer program which will generate isopleths of pollutant concentration for the area covered by the receptor grid to produce a pollution map such as that shown in Figure 6.11.

A great many assumptions have been made in this work to simplify the basic dispersion theory which is itself far from ideal. Many empirical modifications are included which are based on experimental data that may not be typical of all situations and which, inevitably, contain experimental errors. Similarly, the data from which emission rates are calculated may not now be representative of UK traffic. Other, more or less significant errors and approximations may easily be found.

It is important, therefore, that any results obtained by the method be interpreted carefully. It would be unwise, for example, to consider concentrations unacceptable because this model showed a likely exposure to exceed a guideline by a few per cent or, conversely, to dismiss the impact of a road completely if the guideline is a few per cent higher than the predicted exposure. A better assessment may be made by a comparative use of the model. At a site where the road development is shown to increase levels which are already high, there is obviously cause for concern. Where levels are presently low and will not be much changed by a development there is not. Intermediate cases will no doubt occur where interpretation of the results is much more difficult, but again by comparing the model predictions with the existing situation it should be possible to assess whether any action is needed.

6.3.3 Graphical method (Waterfield and Hickman, 1982)

This method uses a set of graphs constructed from the computer model and takes into account vehicle flow, vehicle speed and distance of the receptor from the roads. Meteorological and other variables, which also have a large effect on pollutant concentrations, are not considered independently because the method provides an estimate of the maximum concentration likely to occur. The result chosen is the highest probable value from a distribution of the 8-hour average concentrations which is based on the average hourly value. Thus, all variations in concentration which result from factors other than traffic conditions and position are implicitly included as those which lead to the highest concentration.

The graphs, given in the reference, show the concentration, of carbon monoxide as a function of the distance between the road and the receptor for a straight road and a roundabout, a speed correction (output of CO decreases as speed increases), and an estimation of the 8-hour concentration which is likely to be exceeded once a year.

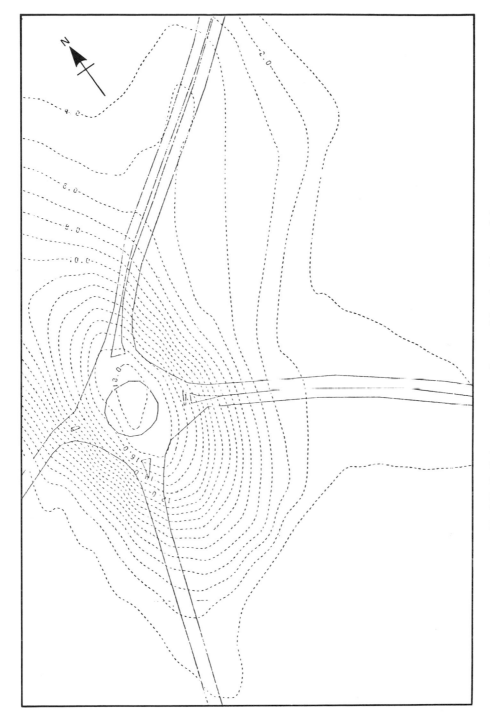

Fig 6.11 Pollution contour map for a road junction with roundabout

147

Use of these graphs gives values for CO concentration, for specific traffic flows and speeds, that have been compared in trials with those obtained from the full computer model for a range of sites. Good agreement has been found, and, as might be expected from the exclusion of the variables noted above, the results from the graphical guide, where they differ from the computer model, tend to be higher in value. It follows that an area subject to high levels of pollution will be unlikely to be missed using the graphical method to provide a preliminary estimate.

6.4   Effects on air pollution of traffic control

Earlier chapters of this review have discussed the effects on exhaust emmissions of different driving models; eg high or low speeds, acceleration or deceleration; and the various test cycles that are in use are intended to replicate these in a range of traffic conditions. It follows that air pollution can be in theory reduced by appropriate traffic control measures, but although this is realised and is implicit in many traffic and road schemes it has not been the subject of direct research.

Now, however, such a research programme is in progress as a co-operative project between the United Kingdom, West Germany, France and Belgium within the European 'DRIVE' research programme. This study is investigating the likely effects of traffic management on air pollution as well as traffic.

There would be little point in going into detail regarding the project at the present time, since at the time of writing it is still at an early stage. However, the plans include, to start with, the instrumentation of a range of 60 cars, petrol and diesel, from small family cars to high performance cars, and heavy lorries, and the measurement and recording of their operating characteristics in different driving environments and different driving modes. This will be certain to improve knowledge concerning the provision of test drive cycles, but it is the intention to go further and to develop a model of exhaust emission rates as a function of vehicle operating conditions. The knowledge thus acquired will be applied to one or more urban areas where it will be possible to investigate changes in traffic control and thereby change the circulation behaviour of the traffic. This will permit the design of alternative traffic systems modified to reduce pollution.

6.5   Chapter 6 References

ASHDOWN ENVIRONMENTAL LIMITED, (1989) Perceived nuisances of vehicle exhaust emissions: a literature review. Transport and Road Research Laboratory, Crowthorne.

BEAR R R and G A WERTHEIM, (1967) Behavioural impairment associated with small doses of carbon monoxide. Am. J. Public Health, *57* (11).

BEVAN M J and A J HICKMAN, (1975) Air pollution in an enclosed car park. TRRL report SR 143. Transport and Road Research Laboratory, Crowthorne.

BRENNAN V H and I S McCRAE, (1988) Pollution levels near a motorway in a cutting. Environmental Meteorology, Grefen and Lobel (eds).

COLWILL D M, (1976) Atmospheric pollution from vehicle emissions: Measurements in Reading, 1971. TRRL Report LR541. Transport and Road Research Laboratory, Crowthorne.

COLWILL D M and A J HICKMAN, (1973) The concentration of volatile and particulate lead compounds in the atmosphere: measurements at four road sites. TRRL Report LR545, Transport and Road Research Laboratory, Crowthorne.

COLWILL D M and A J HICKMAN, (1979) Exposure of drivers to carbon monoxide. Proc 72nd Annual Meeting of the air Pollution Control Association, Ohio.

COLWILL D M, A J HICKMAN and V H WATERFIELD, (1984) Exhaust emissions from cars in service - changes with amendments to ECE Regulation 15. TRRL Report SR840. Transport and Road Research Laboratory, Crowthorne.

DORLING T A and E J SULLIVAN, (1980) Airborne particulate lead levels in Central London 1973-1979. Department of Industry, Warren Spring Laboratory, LR366(AP).

HICKMAN A J, (1976) Atmospheric pollution measurements in West London 1973. TRRL Report LR709. Transport and Road Research Laboratory, Crowthorne.

HICKMAN A J, (1989) Personal exposures to carbon monoxide and oxides of nitrogen. TRRL Report RR 206. Transport and Road Research Laboratory, Crowthorne.

HICKMAN A J, (1989) Measurement of particulate lead on the M4 motorway at Harlington, Middlesex (Fifth report) TRRL Report 184. Transport and Road Research Laboratory, Crowthorne. (Earlier reports 1974, 1976, 1981, 1984).

HICKMAN A J M, G BEVAN and D M COLWILL, (1976) Atmospheric pollution from vehicle emissions: Measurements at four sites in Coventry 1973. TRRL Report LR695. Transport and Road Research Laboratory, Crowthorne.

HICKMAN A J and D M COLWILL, (1982) The estimation of air pollution concentrations from road traffic. TRRL Report LR1052. Transport and Road Research Laboratory, Crowthorne.

HOGBIN L E and M G BEVAN, (1976) Measurement of particulate lead on the M4 motorway at Harlington, Middlesex (Second report). TRRL Report 716. Transport and Road Research Laboratory, Crowthorne.

HOSKO M J, (1970) The effect of carbon monoxide on the visual evoked response in man. Arch. Environ. Health, *21* 174-180.

JOUMARD R, R VIDON and J P GUITTON, (1983) Influence due diesel sur les teneurs en particules - mesurs a Marseille, Mars 1983. Inst. de Recherche des Transports, NNP 75.

LONDON BOROUGH OF SOUTHWARK, (1984-85) Southwark air quality, April 1984 - March 1985.

McCRAE and A J HICKMAN, (1989) Air pollution from traffic in topographically complex locations. Proc. 3rd Int. Symposium on Highway Pollution, Munich, FRG, September.

McFARLAND R A, (1973) Low level exposure to carbon monoxide and driving performance. Arch. Environ. Health. 27 355-359.

RAMSEY J M, (1970) Oxygen reduction and reaction time in hypoxic and normal drivers. Arch. Environ. Health, 20 597-601.

REPORT OF THE ADVISORY COMMITTEE ON TRUNK ROAD ASSESSMENT (1977) Chairman: Sir George Leitch. H M Stationery Office, London.

URY H K, N M PERKINS and J R GOLDSMITH, (1972) Motor vehicle accidents and vehicular pollution in Los Angeles. Arch. Environ. Health, 25 314-322.

WATERFIELD V H and A J HICKMAN, (1982) Estimating air pollution from road traffic: a graphical screening method. TRRL Report SR 752 Transport and Road Research Laboratory, Crowthorne.

WRIGHT G, P RANDELL and R J SHEPHARD, (1973) Carbon monoxide and driving skills. Arch. Environ. Health, 27 349-354.

7 Summary and Conclusions

In the first Chapter transport, as a consumer of fuels which are sources of air pollution, is put into context with other consumers in the United Kingdom, and it is shown that it is second only to power stations. In 1987 some 30 million tonnes of fuel was consumed by transport as compared with about 90 million tonnes by power stations.

Chapter 2 lists exhaust gas pollutants as carbon monoxide and dioxide; lead; oxides of nitrogen; hydrocarbons; sulphur dioxide; and carbon particles (smoke). Secondary problems such as odour and 'smog' are also noted. Methods of measuring these pollutants are described, both in the phase of exhaust emission and as air pollution. Lead is being rapidly removed with the world-wide encouragement of the use of unleaded petrol.

National and international legislation concerned with limiting exhaust emissions is described in Chapter 3, most of which is concerned with pollutants in the vehicle exhaust phase. The problems of defining air quality standards involve health, subjective and ecological effects, and these complications have meant that in most countries air quality itself is not given the attention that is given to exhaust emissions as produced by the vehicle.

Chapter 4 discusses environmental effects including possible damage to health by pollutants such as those of lead and carbon monoxide; subjective effects; and ecological problems such as "acid rain" and the "greenhouse effect". A remarkable change in recent years is that carbon dioxide, which is a product of good combustion and was once thought of as a benign material (in the words of a recent car advertisement just the gas that makes "drinks fizzy"), is now known to be potentially the most dangerous of all in that it does not threaten only those in close proximity to vehicles, but everyone over the whole planet.

Chapter 5 describes how the design of engines affects exhaust emissions, including the use of catalytic converters and "lean-burn" techniques. It also shows the costs of employing various techniques, to manufacturers and ultimately to users and consumers. A Table shows that less CO_2 is produced by diesel than by petrol, and still less by LPG and methanol. Some at present relatively small scale research and development is directed towards virtually pollution-free systems such as hydrogen-powered engines, although if this is to be a complete success the hydrogen itself needs to be produced using some pollution-free generating process to make the electricity.

Field surveys of air quality are described in Chapter 6, together with methods of predicting the concentration of pollutants in the air, emanating from any specified network of roads and pattern of traffic flows. Changes in traffic flow will change the pattern of emissions, and the chapter also mentions a new internationally-based study to investigate the extent to which air quality might be improved by traffic control measures.

It can be concluded from this review that the methods that are available to reduce or eliminate air pollution from exhaust emissions are:

1.   *Short term (present vehicles)*

     (a)   Encourage the use of unleaded petrol.
     (b)   Enforce and reduce speed limits.

2.   *Medium term (modified present vehicle design)*

     (a)   Complete the removal of lead.
     (b)   Use catalytic converters and/or lean burn for petrol engines.
     (c)   Tighten pollution limits for diesel engines.
     (d)   Improve traffic flow.
     (e)   Introduce fuel efficiency standards.

3.   *Long term*

     (a)   Tighten fuel efficiency standards.
     (b)   Develop pollution-free vehicles.

The increasingly severe limits on emissions, and the imminent adoption of 3-way catalysts on petrol engines, will greatly reduce the rate of production of CO, HC and NO_x. Diesel emissions too will come increasingly under the spotlight, though since they cannot be used with reducing catalysts there is a question mark over how much NO_x output from diesels can be reduced, and also it is not clear how much it is practicable to reduce diesel particulates. In the short-term there is considerable scope for improvement, but in the longer term it seems likely that growth in the vehicle fleet will eventually overtake the reduction in exhaust pollutants.

Meanwhile, concern about the 'standard' pollutants from internal combustion engines is being overtaken by consideration of the role of exhaust emissions in the greenhouse effect. The question of fuel efficiency and alternative fuels seems likely to return to centre stage, and there may be tensions between the need to reduce CO_2 production, on the one hand, and the various other pollutants, on the other. In time pollution due to exhaust emissions arising from burning fossil fuel will disappear when we run out of viable quantities of such fuels, and transport will have to rely on other forms of energy. In the meanwhile, emissions from our current technology have to be reduced to a level where they cannot cause irreparable damage to an environment for which the limits of tolerance are gradually becoming clear.

Printed in the United Kingdom for HMSO
Dd. 293371   2/91   C15   3390/3   5673   135477